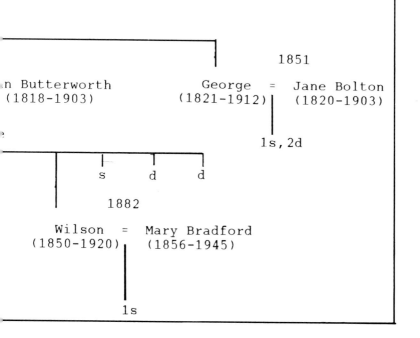

1851

n Butterworth   George   =   Jane Bolton
(1818-1903)   (1821-1912)   (1820-1903)

1s,2d

s   d   d

1882

Wilson   =   Mary Bradford
(1850-1920)   (1856-1945)

1s

THE WORSDELLS

A QUAKER ENGINEERING DYNASTY

Dedicated to the memory of three people who did not live to see the publication of this book:

Elisabeth Lattimer (née Worsdell)
H. M. Lattimer
and Paul Hunt

THE WORSDELLS

A QUAKER ENGINEERING DYNASTY

by
Geoffrey Hill

The Transport Publishing
Company

© **February 1991**

Published by
The Transport Publishing Company

ISBN 86317 158 3

Produced for the Publishers by
Mopok Graphics
128 Pikes Lane
Glossop, Derbyshire

Printed in Great Britain

CONTENTS

Wilson Worsdell's 'R' class No. 2019 crossing the High Level Bridge at Newcastle.

(By Courtesy of the National Railway Museum, York)

I

INTRODUCTION

This work is a short biography of six members of a distinguished family of engineers, the Worsdells, prominent particularly in railway matters in the 19th and early 20th centuries.

The first subject of study, Thomas Clarke Worsdell II (1788-1862), joined the Religious Society of Friends, or Quakers, as a young man. This action would have had a profound effect on the way of life of himself and his descendants and to a great extent, as we shall see in Chapter II, on their choice of careers, many occupations in the 19th Century still being closed to members of that community.

Thomas Clarke Worsdell II was a coachmaker who, after moving from London to Lancashire, set up in business on his own account and was later to assist the famous George Stephenson, constructing the carriages for the opening of the Liverpool and Manchester Railway from 1827 onwards. He also built the wooden tender for the celebrated locomotive 'Rocket', the winner of the 'Rainhill trials' of October 1829.

His eldest son, Nathaniel (1809-1886), assisted his father as a coachmaker in the early days of the Liverpool and Manchester Railway and was to give no less than 52 years service to that company and its successors, the Grand Junction Railway and the London and North Western Railway, mainly at Crewe. He is notable for having invented the device for the automatic pick up and setting down of mail to and from trains at speed.

A second son, Thomas (1818-1893), also received a training in the new skills of railway engineering, followed his father as engineer in charge of locomotives and rolling stock of the Leipzig and Dresden Railway, and on return to Britain set up a successful business producing mainly railway equipment in Birmingham. A gifted inventor, he patented a machine for making and folding envelopes as well as a number of devices for improving railway safety.

The third son, George (1821-1912), was another to make a reputation in the railway engineering trade. He too spent a period of his young manhood working on the Leipzig and Dresden Railway. In 1845 he founded the Dallam Forge at Warrington where he rolled the first bar of iron to be produced in Lancashire with his own hands. His works was awarded a medal at the Great Exhibition of 1851 for the excellence of its iron and of its railway equipment. A combination of ill health and financial difficulties forced him to relinquish the business but it continued to expand and formed the basis of the later Pearson and Knowles Coal and Iron Company Ltd which in turn was to be a constituent of the giant Lancashire Steel Company. The furnaces at Dallam Forge, for many years the largest employer of labour in Warrington, were in operation until 1980 representing 135 years of continuous metalworking on the site.

Two of Nathaniel Worsdell's sons, Thomas William (1838-1916), generally referred to hereafter as William, and Wilson (1850-1920), were to achieve great distinction as railway engineers, most notably in the field of locomotive design. After a Quaker education both young men left their home in Crewe gaining some years experience on the Pennsylvania Railroad in the USA, before returning home to service on the London and North Western Railway. William was works manager at the Crewe Locomotive Works before serving successively the Great Eastern Railway at Stratford, London and the North Eastern Railway at Gateshead as the Locomotive Superintendent. A considerable innovator he is remembered for his championship of the two cylinder compound locomotive type. His engines were also noted for the beauty of their lines and for their commodious and comfortable driving cabs well ahead of their time and which reflected a typical Quaker concern for the welfare of employees. His younger brother, Wilson, also served the North Eastern Railway at Gateshead, firstly as Chief Assistant to his elder brother and finally stepping up on the latter's retirement in 1890. Wilson in turn retired as Chief Mechanical Engineer of the North Eastern Railway in 1910 after 27 years service to the company.

As far as can be told the Worsdell family originated in the Devizes area of Wiltshire. They can be traced with certainty from a Thomas Worsdell born there in 1716, but parish registers and other records in the town show Worsdells in the area before this date. A John Worsdell was baptized in Devizes on August 23rd 1612. This was probably the John Worsdell who married Joan Flower in the town on May 21st 1633. A Nicholas Worsdell married Mary Case here on January 15th, 1664. Several children were born to them: Mary (baptized in 1665), John (1667), Jane (1668) and Mary (1670). A John Worsdell, possibly Nicholas' son above, was married to Deborah Brewer on 12th May 1691. This John died in 1699, his estate being administered by his widow Deborah and by Thomas Worsdell. A Thomas Worsdell, possibly the same gentleman, administered the estate of his wife Mary Worsdell in 1713.

The Thomas Worsdell born on 17th June 1716 and mentioned above is the first member of the family listed in a family Bible which bears an inscription suggesting that it dates from 1630. It is likely therefore that some or all of the earlier Worsdells were ancestors of this Thomas Worsdell.

Thomas, a nurseryman by trade, married Ann Clarke, born in 1721, on the 24th September 1743 at Devizes. There were three sons and at least one daughter of the marriage; the eldest, William (born 1745) was a silversmith who spent most of his life in Holland living at Amsterdam and later Haarlem. A second son, Thomas Clarke, was born in 1748 and the third, Henry, in 1751. A daughter, Alice, was born in 1756 and, according to a recollection of great nephew George Worsdell, there was another daughter. These ladies it is said, married a Mr Neild and a Mr Pepys. Both of these names will recur as the story of the 'engineering Worsdells' unfolds.

Thomas Worsdell was evidently not fortunate in business, a notice in the 'Gentleman's Magazine' in 1768 telling of his bankruptcy. His second son Thomas Clarke Worsdell, (the First), however, followed in the same professional footsteps being variously described as a nurseryman or market gardener. He was in business at Hayes in Kent and it was there that his wife Elizabeth bore him three children; George born in 1777, Elizabeth in 1783 and Thomas Clarke Worsdell (the second) in 1788. Thomas Clarke Worsdell I spent several more years in Hayes after the birth of his children, however, for we know that his youngest son was sent to school in nearby Beckenham. It was probably in the late 1790s that he moved to London, first as a fire insurance agent to the 'Hand in Hand' company and later running the 'Vine Inn' at Kentish Town. His eldest son, George, had died in 1787 at the age of ten and only Elizabeth and the young Thomas Clarke Worsdell II made the move with their parents from Kent to London. As will be seen in Chapter III young Thomas was fortunate to obtain an apprenticeship to a firm of London coachbuilders. It was the pursuit of this career that was soon to lead Thomas to rapidly industrialising Lancashire and to Quakerism, and along with three of his sons into an explosively growing industry — the railways.

II

QUAKERISM, ENTERPRISE AND INNOVATION

'Industry, frugality, temperance and honesty.'

Sometime around 1812 Thomas Clarke Worsdell II decided, on medical advice having recovered from Scarlet Fever, to leave London and his employment as a coachmaker in the Long Acre area near Covent Garden. According to family legend he had secured a position with a coachbuilder, Jonathan Dunn of 'Preston & Lancaster', and at the age of 23, together with his wife Elizabeth and three children under 5 years of age, travelled by canal from London to Runcorn and thus to Liverpool "and walked from there to their destination".

Their journey was doubly significant. Firstly, it took the family to the North West where successive generations were to play such a significant part in railway development throughout the remainder of the 19th century, and secondly, it was shortly after arriving in Lancashire that the couple first encountered members of the Religious Society of Friends (Quakers). Certainly by the time Sarah, their fourth child was born on 15th August 1816 Thomas (and possibly Elizabeth) had joined the 'Friends'. Sarah and her younger brothers Thomas and George, of both of whom much later, all appear in the Births Digest of the Lancashire Quarterly Meeting of Friends.

Membership of the Friends at this time would have carried with it consequences not just in terms of adherents' social relations — the values, attitudes and behaviour associated with Quakerism — but also as regards choice of career. In the early years of the 19th century the latter was still quite severely circumscribed by legislation passed one hundred and fifty years before aimed at 'Non-conformists' in general and often at Quakers in particular.

As early as the 1580s 'independents' had sought greater freedom of thought and expression within a Protestant framework. These people were

Briggflatts Meeting House, Sedbergh, the burial place of Nathaniel and Mary Worsdell, played a prominent part in the religious life of the Worsdell family.

not anti-monarchist as such but disliked the fusion of power between church and monarchy. The Crown, particularly in the form of James I, vigorously asserted the 'Divine Right of Kings' and resisted any pressure for the reform of the Church. The 'independents' however possessed considerable wealth and power. They were able, for example, to found Sidney Sussex College at Cambridge in 1596 as an expressly Puritan foundation. Its students were drawn from the sons of the new landowners and traders who had grown to prosperity after the dissolution of the monasteries. These young men were expected to enter the Church and fight vigorously in the Puritan tradition resisting all popery and frivolity. The Cambridgeshire born Oliver Cromwell was a Sidney Sussex graduate.

The reign of Charles I and his Catholic wife Henrietta Maria saw the addition of many Catholic trappings to church ritual as well as an oppressive increase in taxation. The stage was thus set for the struggle between Parliament and the monarch which culminated in the Civil War and the execution of the King.

George Fox (1624-91) the son of a Calvinistic Leicestershire weaver and churchwarden was initially apprenticed to a shoemaker and sheep, wool and cattle dealer, but at the age of 19, during the Civil War, he set off to travel the land in search of the 'truth'. After several years of frustration seeking help from both the Established Church and Dissenters, and of self examination often close to despair, the 'light' came to him. He evolved a coherent theological system based on personal conviction rather than on received authority. Moreover he taught that the experience of sanctification that he had had was one that everybody could share. From 1648 onwards he began to gather people around him particularly from the Baptist congregations of the Trent Valley. By 1650 Fox had managed to alarm and antagonise the Inquirers of Cromwell's New Model Army and was gaoled, an indignity he had previously suffered at the hands of the King, at Derby. Upon release he travelled extensively in the North West and gathered a group of sixty zealous believers, the 'First Publishers of Truth'. From the early 1650s Fox and his followers proved extremely disruptive particularly in churches and against the 'corrupt' clergy. There was a strong hysterical element in this denunciation, the protesters often trembling and howling as if in a trance and the term 'Quakers' came to be attached to the group.

These Quakers kept up a continual campaign of civil disobedience for some thirty years and found themselves persecuted and legislated against both under the Republic and after the Restoration in 1660. Quakers typically refused to address magistrates or senior churchmen by their honorific titles allowing them only the courtesy 'Sir'. They habitually refused to take off their hats when confronted by their 'betters' and refused to swear oaths (on the wholly reasonable grounds that one was bound to tell the truth at all times). They particularly refused to pay tithes which gave the clergy the opportunity to persecute them. Their refusal to pay fines imposed in the courts frequently gave rise to the most severe distraint of their possessions.

In February 1655 Cromwell passed an ordinance prohibiting the disturbance of ministers and christians in assemblies. Powers were provided to punish Quakers who transgressed. Many were imprisoned, put into stocks and whipped.

After the Restoration, under Lord Chancellor Clarendon, the situation of the Quakers worsened markedly. A series of measures of increasing severity were enacted against them and other 'Non-conformists'. The Corporation Act of 1661 required all mayors, aldermen, councillors and holders of civic posts to communicate in the Church of England. The Quaker Act of 1662 laid down penalties for maintaining that oath taking was contrary to the will of God, for refusing an oath or encouraging others to do so. The printing of any defence of these views was proscribed. In addition any dissident religious meeting of more than five people was banned. All non-conformist groups, not only Quakers, were harshly persecuted under this Act. On a third conviction an offender could be transported. The Act of Uniformity, also of 1662, required clergy to comply with the Book of Common Prayer and resulted in 2,000 Puritan ministers being ejected from their livings.

The first Conventicle Act of 1664 stiffened the Quaker Act to include all 'Non-conformists' after a Puritan uprising in the north the year before. The Act banned all religious meetings other than those of the Established Church, dispensed with jury trial in such cases and increased penalties. It forced Dissenters to meet secretly or not at all. The Five Mile Act of 1665 forbade 'non-conformists' to live or build chapels within five miles of any corporate town.

After the fall of Clarendon a second Conventicle Act turned the screw further. Conviction was now in the power of a single justice. New offences of preaching at a conventicle or harbouring one were introduced. Powers of rapid distraint of property allowed the prospect of financial ruination to replace transportation as the chief deterrent. The increased use of physical violence, through the militia, against both adherents and meeting houses was a feature of the implementation of this Act. Finally the Test Act of 1673 required all holders of public office to take the sacrament in Anglican churches, thus excluding 'Non-conformists' (and Roman Catholics) from office.

This battery of legislation as well as criminalising Quaker meetings severely limited both the area of residence and the employment of Quakers. These penalties remained in force to a substantial degree into the 19th century despite the emollient Toleration Act of 1689, introduced under William and Mary, which removed many of the penal sanctions and allowed liberty of conscience. The Test and Corporation Acts notably remained in force restricting the world of universities and public service to members of the Church of England. They were not repealed until 1829 and 1871 respectively. The Quaker and Non-conformist (or Five Mile) Acts had remained on the statute book until 1812.

The continual persecution in the second half of the 17th century led Quakers to moderate their zeal and conduct themselves with more circumspection. It was at this time that the structure of meetings, still adhered to at the present day, developed. The practise of holding the greater part of such meetings in silence even under provocation and

13

physical assualt from outsiders was a dignified and effective way of ensuring survival in the face of a hostile establishment (later legislation made even meeting in silence a risky proposition). This 'quietism' was to become central to Quaker culture in its great period of development in the 18th century but it cannot be said to be solely a result of a desire for self preservation. Fearful that they might fall into the way of speaking for themselves rather than God they opted to favour silence rather than ministry as the basis for meetings.

The passage of the Toleration Act blunted the fierce stance against the Established Church and in a sense Quakerism became less of a 'movement' and more of an 'organisation' under the control of elders. Great emphasis was placed on the education and indoctrination of those born within the fold. In short Quakers became introspective during the eighteenth century resulting in the development of a distinctive culture and system of beliefs.

Quakers rejected the dictates of fashion favouring simplicity and wearing clothes of such an extreme plainness of colour and style as to be easily recognisable. There were always backsliders though, even amongst Friends, and regular exhortations against this or that vanity had to be issued. A thoroughgoing puritan hostility to the arts was also evident. Singing per se was not considered harmful, but the sentiments expressed in most songs were apt to be deemed unsuitable. Instrumental music, while pleasant in itself, involved long hours of study and practise which were better spent on more important matters. The theatre, the visual arts and novels were similarly proscribed as not conforming to the standards of the gospel in respect of sincerity and truthfulness. Informing all these positions was a firmly held view of how Quakers should occupy their time, a fundamental belief about what people were on earth for and how life should be lived.

The formalisation of administrative procedures in the 18th century served incidentally to foster the growth of a mode of life separate from the rest of society. In the early days there was no formal membership even, the shared experience of persecution conferring belonging. Eventually in 1737 pastoral rather than doctrinal pressures concerned with the responsibilities of trusteeship of money and property required that rules be drawn up so that members might be identified with a particular meeting. For the first time children were enrolled to meetings by virtue of their birth. Thus 'birthright' Quakers soon came to outnumber committed converts and the movement retreated from its position as an outgoing missionary church and took on the character of an exclusive community apart.

One result of this development was the foundation of Quaker schools. One such, Ackworth, near Pontefract in Yorkshire, opened in 1779, was to feature prominently in the education of several generations of the Worsdell family. Another product of separateness was the vital importance of marrying within the community. Inter-marriage between prominent Quaker families was a significant factor in fostering business ties from the 18th century onwards.

An understanding of the ethos of Quaker business is important in the story of the Worsdell family and deserves examination in some depth. As we have seen Quakers were by legislation prevented from entering the legal and academic professions or from taking any office of benefit under the Crown or, indeed, any public office throughout the 18th century. In addition, frequent distraints of their possessions inclined them towards activities such as trade and manufacturing where confiscated stocks could be readily replaced. Certain trades were barred to them by scruple however, such as arms manufacture, the fashion trades, any shipping business protected by arms, or dealing in slaves.

Other aspects of Quakerism too steered them towards trade. The lack of dogma and the importance of contemplation tended to produce the selfawareness and discipline required for entrepreneurial success. Furthermore the intellectual curiosity of Quakers naturally predisposed them towards manufactures where technical innovation played an important role. In such areas the skills and crafts required were new and had not yet been 'professionalised' into institutions and guilds with their concomitant linkages with the 'establishment' of Crown and Church. This interest in new techniques thus gelled perfectly with the Quakers status as outsiders. Capital came to be available within the Quaker community itself as the thrifty pioneer industrialists developed banking interests.

Most importantly, the self imposed ordinances on swearing oaths and signing contracts ruled out any recourse to law as a remedy for business disputes and necessitated the cultivation of an impeccable reputation for straightforwardness and plain dealing in all transactions. A picture is thus emerging of the Quaker entrepreneur or tradesman. He was an austere figure but of charitable impulse, industrious and frugal, honest and sober. As a manufacturer he was liable to be in the forefront of technological innovation; as an employer his beliefs about his fellow man led him to be an enlightened if paternalistic interest in the physical and spiritual welfare of his staff. Indeed the names of Quaker industrialists of the 18th and 19th century provide a roll call of reformers in the fields of improved housing, penal reform, the abolition of slavery and educational provision.

The Victorian extended family: T. W. Worsdell and his wife Mary (centre), his formidable father-in-law Richard Batt (behind them), Edwin and Elizabeth Worsdell (left front) and Wilson Worsdell (far right), taken in about 1888.

The influence of Quakers on industrial development was out of all proportion to their actual numbers. At no time, it is estimated, did they exceed 1% of the total population but the range of enterprise undertaken was staggering. The Darbys of Shropshire were the first people to successfully smelt iron with coke and laid the foundations for the modern iron and steel industries. The Lloyds originated in the metal trades and later in Birmingham founded the banking empire. The Peases of Darlington, originally combers, weavers and buyers of wool moved into collieries and then banking. They hired George Stephenson to advise on the transportation of coal from their pits to the coast and were thus responsible for the construction of the Stockton and Darlington Railway, the first locomotive worked public railway, which opened on 27th September 1825. Indeed throughout the 19th century, Quakers were frequently to be found amongst the promoters of railways often, thanks to their reputation for honesty, as bankers or treasurers.

The Cadburys, Rowntrees and Frys all entered the manufacture of cocoa and chocolate, the Crosfields of Warrington (related by marriage to the Worsdells) soapmaking, the Huntleys and the Palmers biscuit making, the Clarks of Somerset shoemaking, the Barclays of Scotland and Essex banking. Other household names with their origins in Quaker enterprise include Bryant and May (matches), Wedgwood (china), Allen and Hanbury's (pharmaceuticals), Truman, Hanbury and Buxton, and Barclay, Perkins (brewing) and Reckitts, whose 'blue' gave an extra sparkle to the Edwardian washday.

The Hornimans who dealt in tea, William Cookworthy the father of the Cornish China Clay industry, George Bradshaw the founder of the railway guide and John Bright MP, the apostle of free trade, were all Quakers.

Whatever their chosen trade Friends shared the reputation for energy, innovation, high mindedness and above all for giving value for money and for complete integrity. This latter had certainly been well established by the 18th century by which time the names of Lloyd, Pease, Backhouse, Gurney and Barclay had all become familiar in the world of banking. Quaker business was strengthened by the frequent intermarriage between leading families resulting from the 'separateness' and the associated prohibition of 'marrying out'. Thus John Bright's family intermarried with the Clarks and the banking Barclays. The latter were connected with the Gurneys by marriage who were related to the Buxtons and to the Backhouses and the Frys.

Quaker business grew and flourished and therein lay a problem. Development was such that it outstripped the ability of even the large

FRIENDS' MEETING HOUSE · YEALAND CONYERS

Yealand Conyers Meeting House where T. W. Worsdell and his wife Mary Ann were married in 1865 and where they are both buried.

Victorian extended families to produce enough sons to manage the enterprises. Gradually non-Quaker personnel had to be recruited to help manage the burgeoning firms. In addition, the Joint Stock Acts of the 1850s and 60s ushered in the era of the external shareholder and it became the norm to raise capital by share issue rather than by internally generated funds as in the case of the previous family partnerships. By these two paths control thus gradually slipped away from the founding families to the new breed of professional managers and often remote shareholders. Independent Quaker enterprise reached its peak by about 1860 after which many firms were reconstituted as public companies. Lloyds Bank became a public company in 1865. The Coalbrookdale Company (the Darbys' enterprise) was incorporated in 1881, Crosfields in 1896 and so on.

Quaker firms though joining the mainstream of industrial life in the late 19th and early 20th centuries still retained a distinctive 'feel' in many cases, particularly in the area of staff welfare, which has persisted to the present time. Three of the Worsdells whom we are studying, Thomas Clarke Worsdell II and his sons Thomas and George, founded their own companies which would certainly have been run according to the principles outlined above. Regrettably very little has survived to illuminate the social aspects of the way these particular businesses were organised, our knowledge being more or less confined to the nature of the business carried on and the products made.

III

THE RAILWAY PIONEERS

Thomas Clarke Worsdell II and Nathaniel Worsdell
'The best coachbuilder I ever knew'

Thomas Clarke Worsdell II, hereafter 'Thomas Clarke' whose canal journey to the north introduced the previous chapter, was born in Hayes, Kent on 3rd December 1788 the son of a market gardener, Thomas Clarke Worsdell I (1748-1826) and his wife Elizabeth (née Carter, in 1750). He was one of three children. The family moved to London during Thomas Clarke's childhood, Mr Worsdell Snr keeping the 'Vine Hotel', at Kentish Town, a coaching inn first licenced in 1751. Mr Worsdell Snr's exact role is unclear since it is known that the 'Vine' was leased by its owner Mary Cugnoni to a William Odhams for 60 years in 1795. Odhams is described as a 'civil and obliging landlord' who did very well, appearing as a principal landowner in the area in 1804. Mr Worsdell Snr was presumably either an employee of Odhams' or a sub-lessee. (The present day 'Vine' public house in Highgate Road, Kentish Town dates from the 1930s and occupies the site of the original).

Thomas Clarke Worsdell I was not brought up as a Quaker but his outlook and piety were such that he would have undoubtedly been at home amongst the Friends of the 18th century. In later life, having moved north to Cheshire, he was host to his grandson Nathaniel who was attending school nearby. He was remembered as a man with a great dislike of worldliness enjoining the young schoolboy never to wear 'top boots', which he considered a great vanity.

Thomas Clarke Worsdell I
(1748-1826) and his wife
Elizabeth (neé Carter).

Thomas Clarke Worsdell II
(1788-1862), father of
Nathaniel Worsdell and
grandfather of T. W. and
Wilson Worsdell.

Young Thomas Clarke was apprenticed to the coachbuilders Howe and Shanks of Little Queen Street, Long Acre, riding home to Kentish Town once a week on a donkey which he kept in the saw pit at the works.

In 1807 he married Elizabeth Taylor, four years his senior, at St. Botolph's Church, Aldersgate. She was said to have been unable to read, write, or sew. She bore him three children whilst living in London, the eldest being Nathaniel born on 10th October 1809.

Elizabeth Worsdell (neé Taylor) (1784-1863). Wife of Thomas Clarke Worsdell II.

The date of the family's migration to Lancashire is not known with certainty but was sometime between the birth of the couple's second daughter Martha in 1812 and their third Sarah in 1816. Nor is the location of their first home in the north known for certain despite the family myth of the epic canal journey to the north to work for Jonathan Dunn. Mr Dunn is known to have owned a coach building works in Cable Street, Lancaster as early as 1814 but family legend places Thomas Clarke on his arrival in the north variously in Lancaster or Preston. In the 'Preston version', he and his family were befriended by one William Malley who helped them find lodgings. At about this time too, also in Preston, the family first encountered Friends and got to know them. Thomas Clarke is said to have advanced in Mr Dunn's employment later becoming chief man at his works in Lancaster.

There is some evidence to support this version. Records at Friends House, London reveal that a William and Margaret Malley were in membership of the Preston Monthly Meeting in the 1820's but other known facts suggest a more complex though still incomplete history. Thomas Clarke's daughter Sarah was born not at Lancaster or Preston but at Bolton-le-Moor (modern Bolton) on 15th August 1816 and appears in the Friends' Births Digest. Furthermore the Northern Directory of 1816/1817 lists Worsdell and Veevers of Church Wharf, Bolton as coach and harness makers. The Blackburn, Bolton and Preston Directory of 1818 lists T. C. Worsdell, senior, of Black Horse Street, Bolton as a coachmaker. (The designation 'Senior' is slightly puzzling since Thomas Clarke's second son Thomas was born, also in Bolton, but only on November 8th in that year (1818). It cannot conceivably refer to Thomas Clarke Worsdell I, who although by this time possibly resident in the North of England at Knutsford, Cheshire , where he kept a nursery garden towards the end of his life, was never a coachmaker but variously a market gardener, innkeeper and insurance agent for the 'Hand in Hand' Company).

By 1821 Thomas Clarke and Elizabeth were resident in Preston for their third son, George, was born in that town on 21st May. It is here and later at Lancaster, that the family tradition places Thomas Clarke perfecting the skills that were to come to the attention of George and Robert Stephenson, but clearly he had been in business on his own account in Bolton before this. If Thomas Clarke really did come to Lancashire to work for Jonathan Dunn then it is possible that he lived and worked in the city of Lancaster initially but there is no direct evidence for this that the present writer has found. Bolton appears to be the first point of settlement followed by Preston and then Lancaster. Neither is there any mention in directories of Mr Dunn owning a works at all in Preston despite the assertion in family memoirs of Thomas Clarke's working there for Dunn. If the story of Thomas Clarke joining the Friends at Preston is indeed true then he must have had spells of residence there before and after the time at Bolton. In any event he must have joined Friends between 1812 and 1816 the birthdates of Martha, who was christened, and Sarah, entered as a Friend and born at Bolton. We shall probably never know the full story. The Lancashire County Record office at Preston holds membership lists covering the period 1812-27 for the Lancaster, Preston and Bolton and Edgworth Monthly Meetings but unfortunately none of these contains any subsequent mention of Thomas Clarke Worsdell II and his family.

Thomas Clarke's aunt, Mrs Pepys of Chelsea, died childless leaving him £1,000. This enabled him to leave Jonathan Dunn and set up on his own account in Liverpool in 1827. His works there were immediately successful being noted for the excellence of its products. Through the influence of James Cropper, a Quaker director of the Liverpool and Manchester Railway (LMR), he was asked to build the first passenger carriages for that line at his premises.

The great George Stephenson, appointed in May 1824, was the first engineer of the line but was dismissed by the company in mid 1825 after the bill for the line had failed in its passage through Parliament. He was succeeded by the Rennie brothers, George and John, assisted by Charles Vignoles. They had more success than Stephenson with Parliament and the bill was carried on 5th May 1826. After their triumph, however, the brothers sought conditions that were unacceptable to the company and almost by default George Stephenson was reappointed engineer in July 1826.

Many years later, at the time of his retirement, Thomas Clarke's eldest son Nathaniel recalled that era whilst looking back on his career in the columns of the *Crewe Guardian* and the *Crewe Chronicle* of October 16th 1880. The late Professor W. H. Chaloner collated the following account of a vital meeting between Thomas Clarke and Nathaniel and Stephenson from those journals:-

> "In 1828 two years before the opening of the Manchester and Liverpool Railway, I and my father in consultation with George Stephenson....planned the first railway carriage. Stephenson said to my father and myself, 'Come to tea; and after it we will talk over the railway carriage'. We did so; and Stephenson produced a sketch of what he thought might possibly do for a railway carriage. My father and I being practical coachmakers (for I served an apprenticeship under my father)...George Stephenson said, 'Now what do you think about the sketch? What is your opinion upon it? We suggested certain improvements and Stephenson modified it according to the suggestions we threw out, and quite approved of our alterations; therefore, the first carriage that ever travelled between Manchester and Liverpool was built from that sketch, and I only regret that fifteen years ago a fire occurred in my office at Crewe, in which this original sketch...was burnt".

Very soon Thomas Clarke, later described by Stephenson as 'the best coachbuilder I ever knew', was offered the position of Superintendent of Coaching for the LMR which he accepted, taking charge of the design and layout of new buildings adjacent and to the south of the Crown Street terminus of the railway in 1828. Nathaniel joined his father at Crown Street and the two worked together until 1837 when Thomas Clarke left to take up a post with the fledgling Leipzig and Dresden railway.

Not surprisingly, those first carriages at Liverpool bore a remarkable resemblance to the road coaches for which Thomas Clarke was so renowned. Indeed railway carriages in Britain are often referred to as 'coaches' to this day, in contrast to other countries where they are usually 'cars'. The commonest type of first class vehicle consisted essentially of three road coaches fused into one and mounted on an iron underframe. Each vehicle ran on four wheels of three foot diameter. Each of the three compartments held six passengers sitting on well upholstered seats. Folding footsteps were provided for entraining and a seat was provided for the guard/brakesman on the roof. The upper parts of the carriages were finished in black and the lower parts in yellow with dark lettering. These 'standard' first class carriages were glazed, giving rise to the name 'Glass Coaches', although some open vehicles with curtains were provided for summer use. First class mail coaches seating four passengers per compartment (and sometimes another two in a coupé) also came to form part of the fleet of 'yellow' coaches. In the style of the road coaches of the day each first class carriage was named and it is fortunate that the names of many of these have come down to us. R. H. G. Thomas' book *The Liverpool and Manchester Railway* (Batsford, 1980), from which much of the information on these early carriages has been derived, lists the names of 26 culled from various sources.

Thomas Clarke Worsdell II devised a method of connecting carriages using rope couplings tightened by a wooden rod in the style of a tourniquet, but it seems that the LMR first class carriages were coupled into trains by loose chains at the time of the opening. In 1837, the year that Thomas Clarke left the company, Henry Booth's Patent Connecting Chain involving a screw coupling was adopted for all engines and carriages. It seems that Booth's idea owed more than a little to Thomas Clarke's original 'tourniquet' method.

The second class, or 'blue', carriages were much more spartan. Originally they were simply open wooden trucks containing seats, but soon a division into compartments took place. Two main types emerged; The first were two compartment vehicles with a centre entry and four longitudinal rows of seats. The other type consisted of three compartments with a side door to each and reversible backs to the seats. Both of these types sat 25 to 30 passengers per carriage.

The number of carriages constructed at Crown Street in those early days is

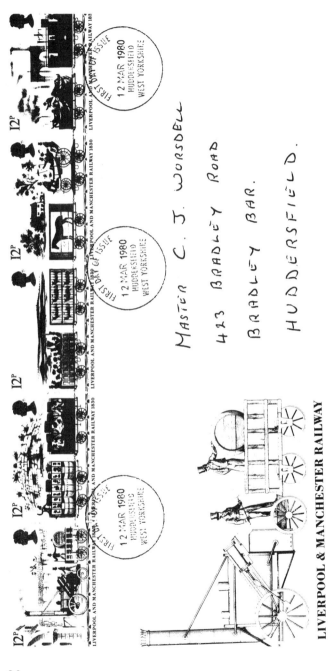

LIVERPOOL & MANCHESTER RAILWAY
Post Office First Day Cover

The first day cover issued in 1980 to commemorate the 150th anniversary of the Liverpool and Manchester Railway illustrates several features attributable to Thomas Clarke Worsdell II. He built the tender for the locomotive *Rocket*, the leading vehicle is one of his first class 'yellow coaches' and the third vehicle is one of the open second class 'blue coaches'.

not known, but there were enough second class vehicles for seven trains at the official opening of the line on 15th September 1830 in addition to that provided for the Duke of Wellington and the principal guests. (The three sumptuous vehicles built for the latter train were, however, not largely the work of the Worsdells, being built up by Edmondson and Company on underframes made at Crown Street). By February 1831 Crown Street could not meet the demand for coaches and orders began to be placed with outside contractors for coach bodies. Nevertheless Thomas Clarke is known to have started building four new first class carriages in December 1831/January 1832. As traffic grew, however, resort to outside coachbuilders again occurred as Crown Street became overstretched and increasingly occupied with improvement and maintenance of the existing stock.

There were a number of such improvements. In 1831 after complaints from second class passengers about burnt clothing, the company deigned to provide roofs to second class carriages. These were of wood or canvass. Further refinements for second class vehicles during the Worsdell era included the fitting of drawbar and buffer springs from January 1833 after the first class carriages had been so equipped. Also in 1833 experiments with gas lighting for carriages were undertaken but these proved unsuccessful.

Replicas of typical first and second class LMR carriages of the Worsdell type were made for the LMR centenary in 1930 and can be seen at the National Railway Museum at York.

Many years later Thomas Clarke's son, Thomas, provided a fascinating glimpse of conditions around the Crown Street works circa 1830. He recalled as a boy seeing his father's carriages being pulled through the Crown Street tunnel by teams of donkeys.

The Crown Street works also produced a variety of wagons for goods traffic. Open platform trucks were used for cotton bales and other goods and pairs of such vehicles employing an early form of articulation were used for timber traffic. Pigs were carried in open six-slatted wagons and two-tiered vehicles with vertical wooden bars for the carriage of sheep were ordered from contractors in 1831. Large numbers of coal and goods wagons were built or acquired by the company leaving aside the large variety of privately owned vehicles which operated on the line. In the early 1830s some coal owners brought coal to the railway in boxes which were fitted on to wagon chassis for transport away. Both boxes and chassis were made at Crown Street and it is interesting to note that coal boxes, though long abandoned on the LMR were still made by Thomas Worsdell at his

Birmingham works in the late 1850s.

By 1833 horse boxes with side flaps lowering to ramps, padded interiors and buffers to reduce jolting had been introduced. This concern for animal welfare is consistent with the Worsdells' Quaker conscience and certainly the young Thomas Worsdell is remembered for similarly humane improvements in livestock wagon design in later years.

The number of wagons owned by the company itself in May 1831 was 300. This had increased to about 460 by 1836. Many of these, particularly in the early days were built at Crown Street by Thomas Clarke's staff but from 1833 onwards wagons, too, were increasingly provided by outside contractors.

Perhaps Thomas Clarke's greatest claim to fame during his time at Crown Street lies in his cooperation with the Stephensons at the time of the 'Rainhill Trials' in October 1829. At this time the company was considering what kind of traction should be used on the line and decided to stage a trial

The 'Rocket' as originally built in 1829, with tender constructed by Thomas Clarke Worsdell II.

STEPHENSON'S "ROCKET" AND TENDER, 1829.

of steam locomotives. The main contestants, were the 'Novelty' of Braithwaite and Ericsson, the 'Sanspareil' by Timothy Hackworth and the 'Rocket' by Robert Stephenson, the son of George, the company's engineer. Robert Stephenson asked Henry Booth, the Secretary, Treasurer and later General Manager of the company, to have the tender for 'Rocket' built in Liverpool "as the coachmakers...will make one neater than our men". As built by Thomas Clarke and his staff, the tender had a strong wooden frame on four cast iron wheels with outside bearings. The coke fuel for 'Rocket' was stored on the floor beneath a 300 gallon water tank. The triumph of 'Rocket' at Rainhill confirmed the desirability of locomotive haulage on the line rather than the use of stationary haulage engines.

Thomas Clarke left the Liverpool and Manchester Railway in January 1837 writing to thank the directors for their encouragement and kindness "for so many years". He had been asked to take responsibility for the whole of the rolling stock (engines, carriages and wagons) of the Leipzig and Dresden Railway and took with him his wife, the younger sons Thomas and George and daughter Sarah. Fortunately some family letters have survived which give a vivid flavour of those early days in Germany. The family "went from Hamburg by a steamer to Magdeburg, took us 3 days and 2 nights and from thence had about 70 English miles to Leipzig, slept half way at an Inn, where they stared at us well and had some curious entertainment, and started at about 4 next morning for Leipzig."

A part of the Leipzig and Dresden line was clearly in operation by the time of Thomas Clarke's letter of June 1837, by which time Sarah had returned to England. He describes how "our train, 10 coaches does run about four days a week...they hoist a national flag on some old buildings, a signal that 'Damphwagon' and coaches will run that day". Thomas Clarke and his sons rapidly set about building up the railway. He looked back to Britain for locomotives, ten coming from the firm of Rothwell and Company of the Union Foundry, Bolton by 1840, another five from William Kirtley of the Dallam Foundry, Warrington in 1837-38 and one from Robert Stephenson in 1838. Carriages and wagons however were made at Leipzig by the Worsdells, the family being immediately engaged in the manufacture of 25 first class, 60 second class, 60 third class carriages and 200 goods wagons. Much of the raw material was to come from "a place called Malkren where they are sawing us a great number of ash trees".

Living conditions, however, were not what Thomas Clarke was used to. Milk, butter and eggs were plentiful enough and he was hopeful of seasonal fruit, but the butcher's meat was considered very inferior in

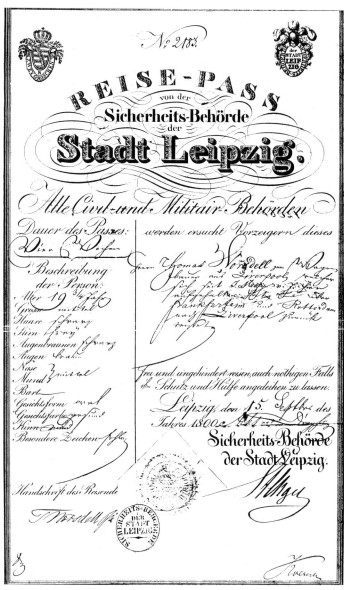

Passport issued to Thomas Worsdell by the authorities at Leipzig, dated 15th September 1838. At this time he and his brother George were assisting their father Thomas Clarke Worsdell II as locomotive and rolling stock engineer on the Leipzig and Dresden Railway.

quality and even the standard of the pens and ink came in for criticism. Indeed he did not scruple to ask Nathaniel back in England to send to John Pownall (his successor as Superintendent at Crown Street) for a variety of stores, which were presumably hard to come by. These included twelve 'Liverpool spoke shaves', a large number of screwdrivers of varying sizes, one pound of best glue, 3 bottles of best Japan ink, 3 bottles of best blue ink in strong stone, 6 lbs of best coffee and 1 lb of good gunpowder!

Thomas Clarke became friends with a local landowner to whom he refers throughout as 'the Baron'. Though clearly a man of some substance who rode around the countryside in a Phaeton, Thomas Clarke thought him a very rough fellow. He was horrified that the Baron claimed to have killed two men whilst in the service of the English Government (from whom he received a pension) and resolved to try to civilise him. "We are going to his house and I shall have the opportunity of trying his hard heart, perhaps a soft appeal might do him good". Prospects on the domestic front were no less fraught for the Baron. One of Thomas Clarke's engineers told that on one occasion the Baron's wife thinking he was about to enter the room took up a basin of water and flung it at the door only to find a visitor entering.

Thomas Clarke's lack of expertise in locomotive engineering matters is revealed in his request to Nathaniel to seek the advice of Jo. Gray on the haulage capacities of locomotives of 12ins. by 18ins. cylinders on a 1 in 70 incline. He was uncertain too, if to allow for double the load if a train was assisted by a second engine. The letters contain a wealth of interesting minutiae. He required a tin pot that will hold an exact pint (Imperial), his wife requested a grid iron, a cat was given away as not house trained on the promise that the new owner would not drown it ,and the chairman of the Leipzig company was to be seduced with two canisters of Lundyfoot snuff to be sent from England! Life was clearly tolerable, Elizabeth had learned a few words of German and their reputation was such that people called out "Damphwagon!" as the boys George and Thomas passed in the streets. Clearly though the enterprise was not without its difficulties. In mid 1837 the company was short of funds and sought to raise another £300,000. A later letter indicates that only fifteen miles of line from Leipzig to Wurzen had been opened to traffic.

Thomas Clarke Worsdell II had returned to England by about 1841 residing at Hull where his son George was working around that time. Later from 1845 he and his wife took up residence at Nantwich near Crewe so as to be near Nathaniel and the grandchildren. He played an active part in local affairs being a member of the Nantwich Meeting of Friends and pursuing a long term interest in homeopathic medicine. He built up a large stock of medicines travelling the countryside around healing the sick. When the county was visited by a serious cattle plague he became convinced that the standard veterinary remedies were inadequate and applied his own homeopathic principles saving the lives of many animals. His grandson William Worsdell recalled that some years after this plague he met a prominent farmer in the locality who swore that if it had not been for his grandfather he would have lost his entire stock, whereas not one that had been treated by him had died. Thomas Clarke's interest in the subject was academic as well as practical. He consulted with orthodox physicians on occasions and his knowledge derived from a wide number of sources.

William Worsdell, born in 1838, remembered visiting his grandparents in Hull at the age of about three. Elizabeth Worsdell was an active little woman wearing a Friends' muslin cap. In later years crippled by rheumatism and virtually confined to a chair by the fire she became rather brisk and short-tempered and definitely not to be trifled with by young grandchildren. She must have been the ideal partner to her husband, however. Remembered lovingly by his grandchildren as a lively and playful man, he was known for his open-hearted benevolence. William had no doubt that if it had not been for the shrewdness of his wife Thomas Clarke would have given away everything he had.

Nathaniel Worsdell (1809-1886) — photographed in Vienna, date unknown — probably c.1850.

In later years the couple travelled frequently to Crewe, in a trap hauled by a pony called Midge, to visit Nathaniel and the grandchildren. They still wore the traditional Quaker costume and presented a quaint spectacle, he tall and thin in a broad brimmed hat, she small and stout in a deep poke bonnet.

Thomas Clarke Worsdell II died on the 18th April 1862 at the age of 73 at Welch Row in Nantwich. Elizabeth though older, survived him by a few months dying on the 12th January following. Both are buried at the Friends' Meeting House, Nantwich.

On 10th February 1881 a dinner was held at the North Western Hotel, Lime Street, Liverpool to honour Nathaniel Worsdell, retiring after 52 years service to the London and North Western Railway and its predecessors. Responding on behalf of the guests Mr. W. Titherington of Chester celebrated a long friendship with both Nathaniel and his father, "more honourable people the world never contained". Recalling that Thomas Clarke Worsdell II had made the first railway carriage in England he told the meeting that carriages built under his direction were, he believed, "at present in use on the Birkenhead Railway, and....it was impossible to drag them to pieces".

Nathaniel had stayed on at Crown Street under John Pownall whilst his father and two brothers sojourned in Leipzig. He was to find his niche in railway history soon after their departure in 1837 as the inventor of the apparatus for picking up and setting down mail from moving trains.

He was, as we have seen, born in London but migrated north with the family as a small child. He was sent to school at Knutsford in Cheshire living there with his grandparents, Thomas Clarke Worsdell I and Elizabeth until his thirteenth year. Subsequently he was apprenticed to the same Jonathan Dunn who employed his father. It seems clear that this was at Lancaster where his father is said to have been working prior to the move to Liverpool. Probability favours Lancaster not least because it is likely that in that town Nathaniel met his future wife, the Ackworth educated Mary Wilson, a native of Bentham in the Yorkshire Dales, close by Lancaster.

Nathaniel joined his father at his Liverpool works at the age of about eighteen soon moving over with him to the employ of the Liverpool and Manchester line in 1828.

The first mail had been carried on a train between Liverpool and Manchester on 11th November 1830 and by 1831 two of the Worsdells passenger coaches the 'Wellington' and the 'Lord Derby' had been converted to carry mail such was the volume of postal business. Very soon a third coach, the 'Fly' was similarly converted. In December 1831 the Post

Office became concerned that guards on trains had adopted the practise of carrying mail on the trains on their own account, thus depriving the Post Office of revenue. It was clear, therefore, that not only was mail carrying becoming an important facet of railway operations but also that some thought needed to be given to the provision of a comprehensive and efficient postal service geared to customer requirements. With the opening of the Grand Junction Railway from Birmingham to meet the Liverpool and Manchester line a further heavy increase in mail traffic was forthcoming and to cope with this a travelling post office featuring on-train sorting was introduced on 6th January 1838 between Birmingham and Liverpool. This first vehicle was a horse box converted for the purpose. In the first few months of operation mail pouches had been thrown between station staffs and the train guard at speed sometimes resulting in either damage to the mail or often, in the case of 'pick up', failure to make contact leading to delays as the train would have to stop and 'back up'.

From late 1838 Nathaniel Worsdell built the first specially constructed mail vans at the Crown Street works. They incorporated his own ideas of an automatic pick up and set down apparatus for mail bags. A description of the apparatus is given in the specification attached to his patent application (No. 7528 of 1838). He was granted Letters Patent on 4th January 1838, enrolled in the High Court of Chancery on 4th July in the same year. At the end of the specification, which can be inspected at the Patent Office Library in Holborn, London, there is a form of words to the effect that on the 30th June 1838 Nathaniel "came before our said Lady the Queen in her Chancery, and acknowledged the specification aforesaid, and all and every thing therein contained and specified, in the form written above."

The original patent granted to Nathaniel, complete with massive seal, is still cherished by one of his great-grandsons.

Nathaniel's apparatus, first tried out at Winsford near Crewe was a very simple one but nevertheless one which led him into prolonged dispute with the Post Office. From the outset the Post Master General represented by Lieutenant Colonel Maberly, showed great interest in buying out Nathaniel's patent. The latter's asking price of £3,500 was, however, turned down flat by the authorities who made an offer of £500. Nathaniel countered with a price of £1,500 which was again rejected. Mr V. Carpinall of the Patent Office thought the invention a very valuable one and suggested to Nathaniel that in his view £3,500 was too low a price. In a letter to Nathaniel dated 16th April 1838, he was very forthright, "the Post Office is certainly governed by most extraordinary persons and the only

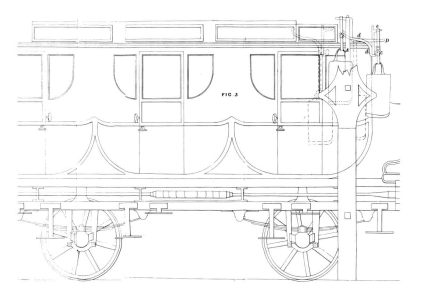

Two drawings illustrating Nathaniel Worsdell's 1838 patent specification for an automatic apparatus for picking up and setting down mail bags at speed.

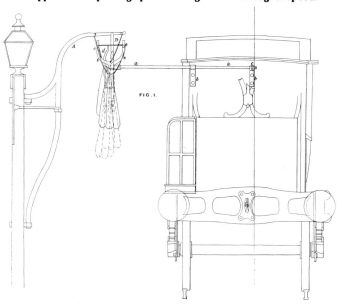

thing to do is to put the invention before the public and shame the Post Office into being reasonable". Mr Carpinall showed a model of the apparatus at a meeting of the Civil Engineers and at the Royal Institution where it was much approved. He advised Nathaniel that "the Post Office will soon see the necessity of applying to you".

This, however, was not to be, for the Post Office in August of the same year introduced their own form of pick up and put down apparatus for mail bags on trains between London and Warrington over the Grand Junction and the London and Birmingham Railways. Later in that year this service was extended to Liverpool (in September) and Preston (in November). The Post Office used 'Ramsey's Apparatus' named after John Ramsey, an officer of their 'missing letter branch'. This apparatus had been tested at Boxmoor on 30th May 1838 and, being deemed satisfactory, instructions were given almost immediately for the erection of lineside standards at Berkhamsted and Leighton Buzzard. The directors of the Grand Junction Railway were in no doubt that this apparatus was in all essentials similar to that of Nathaniel Worsdell and undoubtedly post-dated it. In short that the Post Office was infringing Nathaniel's patent. This was generally considered to be a great injustice and Mr Joseph Pease MP, of Darlington, who had become the first Quaker MP in 1832, interceded on his behalf. In a letter of 17th October 1839 to Maberley he suggested that negotiations be reopened between the Post Master General and Nathaniel. Nothing came of Pease's initiative unfortunately and Nathaniel never received any compensation from the Post Office, not even in respect of the infringement of patent.

Ramsey's Apparatus proved to be rather unsatisfactory in use. Mail bags released from trains were not caught by a lineside standard, as in Nathaniel's apparatus, but fell to the trackside often being swept under the wheels of the train and damaged. This resulted in its replacement on the South Eastern Railway in 1848 by an arrangement devised by John Dicker. Interestingly in this case the Post Office tacitly acknowledged a debt to Nathaniel's design not deeming it prudent to introduce Dicker's apparatus on the LNWR and elsewhere until 1852 when Nathaniel's patent expired. The problem of Crown Immunity notwithstanding, Nathaniel, as a Quaker, would not in any case have had the ready option of recourse to law over the matter. It is perhaps significant that many years later at his retirement banquet the Chairman for the evening Mr George Crosfield, described the guest of honour as 'a Nathaniel indeed in whom there is no guile'.

A reconstruction of one of Nathaniel's original purpose-built travelling post offices of 1838 is amongst the exhibits at the National Railway Museum, York.

This straightforwardness and loyalty were the hallmarks of Nathaniel's life. In all he served the London and North Western Railway and its predecessor companies for fifty two years. Fortunately he has left that account of his career referred to earlier and published in the *Crewe Guardian* and the *Crewe Chronicle* of 16th October 1880. His early years at Crown Street with the Liverpool and Manchester Railway have been described. The move to Crewe came in 1843 with his appointment as manager of the coach-making department of the Grand Junction Railway. He held this post until 1860 when his department was moved by the then London and North Western Railway (LNWR). Staying on in Crewe he took over the Stores Purchasing Department where he worked for twenty two years retiring at the age of 71.

He played an active part in the development of the new railway community at Crewe involving himself in good works from the outset. Soon after his arrival he became the first President of the Crewe Temperance Society, a post he held until 1871 when pressure of work caused him to relinquish it in favour of the vice-presidency which he held until 1880. He was a supporter of the Library and Newsroom Committee which in 1845 was to form part of the Mechanics Institution. Elected Vice-Chairman of the first council of the latter body at the inaugural meeting on 13th September 1845, his involvement with the work of the Institution in the fields of adult and children's education lasted throughout the period of its infancy until 1848.

Nathaniel can also be considered one of the fathers of local government in the town being elected in January 1860 one of the first members of the newly formed Monks Coppenhall Local Board of Health which took over many responsibilities from the former Vestry system of local government. He served on the Local Board for almost four years being proposed and seconded for the Chairmanship at the Annual General Meeting of 1863 held on 27th January. Perhaps rather typically Nathaniel declined, feeling himself unable to attend properly to the duties of office. Later that year, indeed, he resigned from the Board but re-entered local politics in 1877. In June of that year he stood for election as an Independent, along with his son William, to the East Ward of the new Borough of Crewe. He was unsuccessful; gaining 211 votes, William receiving 195.

In November of the same year standing in the South Ward with Liberal support, he was elected with 545 votes. William stood again in the East Ward with Liberal backing and was also successful. Nathaniel served on the Council until his retirement and departure from Crewe to Birkenhead in 1880. In fact he had nailed his political colours firmly to the mast as early as April 1872 chairing a meeting in the town called to form a branch there of the West Cheshire Liberal Association. Always a devout member of the Quaker community he attended the Nantwich meeting of the Friends of which he was recorded a minister in 1865.

He had married Mary Wilson on 3rd October 1833. She was the daughter of Christopher Wilson, a flaxdresser, and of Eleanor Wilson of Bentham, Yorkshire. She bore him thirteen children, only seven of whom survived into adulthood. Interestingly there were two sets of twins, Eliza and Ellen born in 1840 who survived only a matter of days and Leoline and Oswald, in 1849, who were amongst the seven surviving into maturity. Tragically the two youngest, Mary Edith and Isabella Helen died as young children within days of each other in the winter of 1862/3 from diphtheria. The sons of the family were educated at Ackworth School, two of them, William and Wilson, later subjects of this study, going on to become distinguished railway engineers.

Nathaniel and Mary Worsdell had a summer residence called 'Delamere' at Silverdale beside Morecambe Bay in North Lancashire, built to the designs of their eldest son William. Following Mary's death there in 1869, at the age of 57 and after a long and painful illness, the property was sold.

The invitation to Nathaniel Worsdell's retirement dinner in 1881.

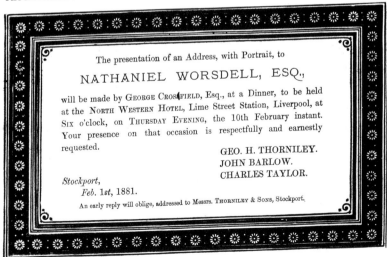

The presentation of an Address, with Portrait, to

NATHANIEL WORSDELL, ESQ.,

will be made by GEORGE CROSFIELD, Esq., at a Dinner, to be held at the NORTH WESTERN HOTEL, Lime Street Station, Liverpool, at SIX o'clock, on THURSDAY EVENING, the 10th February instant. Your presence on that occasion is respectfully and earnestly requested.

GEO. H. THORNILEY.
JOHN BARLOW.
CHARLES TAYLOR.

Stockport,
Feb. 1st, 1881.

An early reply will oblige, addressed to Messrs. THORNILEY & SONS, Stockport.

It was (and is) customary at times of retirement and resignation to honour the departing with some form of presentation. Newspaper reports of such events in Victorian times, whilst containing much predictable verbose adulation, often provided valuable insight into the character of the beneficiary, as well as details of his life in the workplace and in the wider community. The report of the dinner given to honour Nathaniel's retirement is a classic of its kind. The dinner took place at the North Western Hotel, Liverpool on 10th February 1881 and its lavishness and the large number present testify to the esteem in which he was held by the railway and business communities. The *Crewe Guardian* of 12th February reported that some sixty gentlemen were present under the chairmanship of Mr George Crosfield, Chairman of the Stores Committee of the London and North Western Railway. The meal, the extravagance of which may well have shocked the austere Nathaniel, consisted of eight courses and the full menu is given in Appendix V1. The main business of the evening involved the presentation to Nathaniel of a portrait and an illuminated address by a number of the guests, timber merchants in Liverpool, Stockport, Hull, Grimsby and the Midland Counties. The portrait, which was life size, was considered an excellent one and was by Mr Charles Bragger of London who was present. Little is known to the present author of Mr Bragger. The list of exhibitors at the Royal Academy shows that he exhibited there but once, in 1880, a portrait of 'Mr Worrall'. Bragger's address is given as 39B Old Bond Street, London.

In their address, read by Mr George Thorniley of Stockport, the timber merchants paid tribute to Nathaniel's 52 years of service to the company adding that 'we are anxious to perpetuate your name and sterling worth of your character by asking your acceptance of the accompanying portrait as a substantial memento of our respect and esteem, and as an heirloom in your family'. The chairman in his address said to cheers 'his character is unblemished, and there is not a whisper of anything that should induce him to turn to the right hand or to the left'.

Amongst the guests were Francis William Webb, Locomotive Superintendent of the LNWR at Crewe, who proposed the toast to 'the Timber Trade', Nathaniel's younger brothers, Thomas and George (q.v.), his sons, William and Wilson (q.v.) and a third son Edwin. Edwin Worsdell (1845-1930) can perhaps be fairly described as the 'black sheep' of his generation. After a conventional Quaker education at Ackworth he joined a firm of timber merchants in Liverpool and crowned a reputation for 'wildness' by marrying in 1866 Elizabeth Gray, a professional dancer. As well as dismaying his family this action resulted in him being disowned by the Hardshaw West Monthly Meeting of Friends. Edwin and Elizabeth emigrated to Iowa, USA where Edwin farmed for some time, the couple returning to England after he had been incapacitated through sunstroke. Perhaps inevitably he settled down to a long career on the LNWR, serving in the permanent way department, and was reconciled with the family.

In thanking the gathering for the honour it had bestowed on him Nathaniel felt that "if I speak honestly, there is no merit due to me. I have only done that which I believe to be my duty to my employers....whom I have served for 52 years. I believe the......Company is the largest commercial undertaking in the world, commanding very nearly....ten hundred million pounds sterling (sic.). It is a most marvellous undertaking. I have grown up with it, first commencing in the year 1826 (presumably a misprint for 1828), under the auspices of George Stephenson who was my first master".

After Nathaniel's death on 24th July 1886 at Birkenhead the Hardshaw West Monthly Meeting at Liverpool wrote of him thus "He was known in all his business relations as a man of strict integrity and truthfulness. It is related that in the case of an arbitration the parties were advised 'to employ Worsdell, for he will speak the truth if he had to die for it'. For a long period of his life he had control of large bodies of workmen in his dealings with whom he was strict but just, and he ever took a deep interest in their moral and spiritual welfare". His ministry amongst the Quakers was characterised by "great earnestness" but above all he "sought to preach by life as well as by the word". Both Nathaniel and Mary Worsdell are buried at the Friends' Burial Ground at Briggflats near Sedbergh in Yorkshire.

One final story serves to illuminate Nathaniel's conscientious character. A surviving letter written to Mary and dated 29th October 1842 tells how on the way to a Friends' meeting he called in at Liverpool's Lime Street Station only to hear that a train which had left Birmingham early that morning had met with an accident. The last carriage had tipped over with thirteen passengers inside. Fortunately no-one was badly injured, but the guard being unable to give an account of the cause of the accident led Nathaniel to fear some defect of the carriage itself. He set off by the next train for Wolverhampton, where the accident had occurred, to ascertain the facts. On arrival at Warrington Nathaniel's anxieties were soothed by the information that the derailment had in fact been caused by a pig which had fallen from a wagon across the track of the Birmingham train!

IV

THE ENTREPRENEURS

Thomas and George Worsdell

Nathaniel Worsdell's younger brothers, Thomas and George, were clearly of a different temperament to their older sibling. Both possessed considerable entrepreneurial flair and established successful businesses whilst still young men. Unlike Nathaniel both had accompanied their father to Leipzig in 1837 at the ages of 18 and 15 respectively.

Thomas was born on 8th November 1818 at Bolton-le-Moor. Little or nothing is known of his childhood and education but at an early age he demonstrated a talent for engineering winning the £200 prize for the best model of a railway carriage to be adopted for the London and Birmingham Railway, then under construction. Thomas' model 'The Experience' employed the screw coupling for the first time, his own invention and later improved by Henry Booth of the Liverpool and Manchester Railway. The model was built to one third scale being six feet long and had been constructed at the Crown Street works in Liverpool managed by his father. The carriage was of a design which was to remain substantially unaltered for many years. There were some archaic features however as we should expect of a vehicle designed probably in 1834. Luggage was carried on the roof and the guard's seat was outside exposed to the elements. The wheels were of wood with iron tyres at the rims. The model is said to have been sent to London by one of 'Pickford's quick passenger vans' at a cost of £17. It remained at Euston for many years but was eventually moved to Thomas' home at Ulverston where a craftsman was taken on to refurbish it. Regrettably this man left the country at short notice and the vehicle remained in a dismantled state. Eventually, through the good offices of George Worsdell, the model was presented to the London and North Western Railway for inclusion in its collection of historic exhibits at Euston.

ON the *Eighth* Day of the *Eleventh* Month,
One Thousand Eight Hundred and *eighteen* was born *in Bolton, le, moor* — — — — — — — in the Parish *of Bolton* — — — — — — — — in the *County* of *Lancaster* unto *Thomas Worsdell Coach Maker* and *Elizabeth* his Wife, *a Son* who *is* named *Thomas*.

We, who were present at the said Birth, have subscribed our Names as Witnesses thereof.

John Entwistle *Mary Rutherford*

witness to the mark Ann. Entwistle X *her mark*

Certificate of the birth of Thomas Worsdell at Bolton-le-Moor in 1818. The birth was witnessed by Abram Watson, Surgeon, Mary Rutherford and (the illiterate) Ann Entwistle.

Thomas' talents would have made him a great help to his father in Leipzig. In a letter home Thomas Clarke Worsdell II observed that at the time of writing 'Tommy' was engaged upon a drawing (presumably of a technical nature) whilst George studied the language. Thomas must have shown some interest in languages, too, for he is reported to have helped the German lexicographer Flugel, then completing an English/German dictionary, with technical terms. In 1838 at the age of twenty he was offered the post of Locomotive and Rolling Stock Superintendent of the line under his father. He stayed on in Germany after his father and George and the rest of the family returned to England. Certainly he worked subsequently in Berlin and he was in Hamburg in 1842 where he witnessed a great fire. Along with some other Englishmen he attempted to contain the spread of this fire by blowing up some buildings in the path of the flames. Their action was misunderstood by a frightened crowd, who, thinking them guilty of incendiarism, threatened them, requiring their rescue by the local British Consul. Thomas returned to England seemingly in May 1842 and married Ann, the daughter of John Butterworth, of New

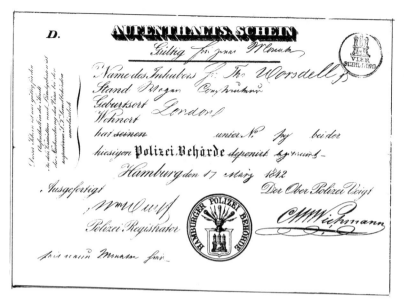

The Police Pass issued to Thomas Worsdell in Hamburg in March 1842. Whilst in the city Thomas attempted, with some English friends, to prevent the spread of a large fire by blowing up buildings in its path.

Street, Lancaster in that city on 17th January 1843. There were to be no children of the marriage.

Thomas was an inventive young man and his time in Leipzig would have enabled him to test himself on a whole range of engineering problems. On his return to England he worked at Stratford, London, probably for the Eastern Counties Railway. By October 1845, however, he had moved to Birmingham and it was from here that Thomas, described as a railway carriage builder, took out his first patent. This specified "an improved construction of apparatus to be applied to railway carriages, for protecting the passengers from injury in the case of collision; and secondly, in an improved construction of jack for lifting heavy bodies, and particularly railway carriages and engines." The 'apparatus' referred to consisted of a padded shield placed across the front end of the carriage and so mounted that in case of collision it would fly up and cover the glass at that part of the carriage, thus saving passengers from being flung into contact with the glass.

43

Thomas Worsdell (1818-1893), the Birmingham engineer in whose workshops were trained his nephew T. W. Worsdell and the celebrated Tangye brothers.

Thomas was not only interested in the safety and welfare of human passengers however. He also devised a method of letting down the sides of goods wagons to allow horses and cattle to detrain by means of a ramp.

In this concern for traveller safety Thomas was very much his father's son. Thomas Clarke Worsdell II in his letters home from Leipzig was much exercised by, and concerned with, accidents on the early railways of mainland Europe, describing no less than three, two on the Vienna Railway and one on the Brussels Railway, in one letter alone.

Thomas set up in business in Birmingham manufacturing his patent lifting jack very soon after being granted letters patent. His name first appears in the Birmingham directories in 1846 with an address at 8 Islington Row. Between 1847 and 1852 his works address was given as Brasshouse Passage and his home address at Wheeley's Row. By 1854 the works had moved to Berkeley Street. From the outset a wide range of engineering products was made with a strong leaning towards railway material. In 1855 Thomas acquired a partner, William Henry Evans, and the two styled themselves as "Worsdell and Evans, railway wagon builders", from then until 1860 with an additional works in Tennant Street.

Amongst the orders received by the firm during this period was one placed in December 1855 by Isambard Kingdom Brunel in his role as Engineer to the Vale of Neath Railway Company. The order was for 250 'coal boxes' for use on the company's flat wagons to be supplied at a cost of £16.6s.9d (£16.34p) each. This early form of containerisation was in fact an archaism imposed on the railway company by the conditions pertaining at that time for the enshipment of coal at Swansea Docks, there being no facilities there for the tipping of complete wagons.

From the time of Evans' departure in 1860 until Thomas' retirement in 1867 the company reverted to the style 'Thomas Worsdell'.

In the year of his partnership with William Evans another patent was granted to Thomas for improvements to "the screw lifting jack known as Haley's Jack, whereby...jacks are rendered more durable in wear and whereby the speed with which the screw can be raised or lowered may be increased". Further modifications resulted in a jack that could be operated both as a lever or screw jack and which, thanks to the fitting of ratchets, would not 'run down' under load. Clearly ten years after the founding of the

An advertisement in *The Engineer* of August 1862 indicates the range of products made at Thomas Worsdell's works.

15, 1862.   THE ENGINEER.

GAS APPARATUS. Works Complete, and Gas TUS in detail, of every description and size. Plans, Specimates prepared for any part of the world. A list of 100 a great number of Gas Works erected by the advertiser— ther particulars, forwarded on application. Patentee of Apparatus, the Combined Gas Purifier, and the Vertical

STEAM ENGINES. Steam Engines.—Vertical and Horizontal—fixed and portable— adapted for all kinds of fuel, up to 20-horse power. Mechanical Engineering work in general tenderod for from plans and specifications.

BOILERS. Boilers.—Cylindrical, Cornish, and Multitubular; made of the best plate, and proved to a high pressure. Kitchen range and hot house boilers. Tanks, girders, and other wrought iron work to drawing.

CASTINGS. Castings executed with dispatch—the patterns taken the care of and returned with the goods at moderate prices.

GEORGE BOWER, Engineer and Contractor, Vulcan Iron Works, St. Neots, Hunts.

THOMAS WORSDELL, Berkeley-street and Granville-street, Birmingham,
INTERNATIONAL EXHIBITION, EASTERN ANNEXE, No. 2031.

Manufacturer of Contractors' Locomotives, Portable and other Steam Engines; Steam, Wharf, Ship, and Travelling Cranes; Hand, Wharf, Travelling, Derrick, and other Cranes; Steam and Hand Crab Winches; Travelling Crabs for Gauntry Frames; Pulley Blocks, &c.
Lathes; Planing, Slotting, Drilling, Screwing, Punching, and Shearing Machines; Ratchet Braces and General Machinery; Wrought Iron Smiths' Hearths, Anvils, Vices, &c.
Lifting Jacks, viz., Traversing, Haley's, Windlass, Tripod, Bottle, &c.; Improved Patent Wrought Iron Hydraulic Jacks, to raise from 4 to 200 tons; Hydraulic Machines to Test Bar Iron, Steel, Chain Cables, and Small Portable for Girders and Wire.
Railway Train Bell Signal Apparatus; Rail-setting Presses, Jim Crows, and other Contractors Tools; Railway Buffers, Screw Couplings, Bolts and Nuts, &c.   (D1207)
STEAM CRANES, LIFTING JACKS, &c., KEPT IN STOCK.

CONTRACTORS LOCOMOTIVE.

M WHARF CRANE.

STEAM TRAVELLING CRA

45

firm jacks were still a major product and continued to be so until at least the 1870's by which time one Richard C. Gibbins was operating from the Berkeley Street works. A very large number of these jacks would have been made, indeed it is said that as late as the end of the First World War some of the breakdown trains on the North Eastern Railway at Darlington still carried jacks with the legend 'Worsdell, Birmingham' cast into them.

Very little information about the earliest days of the firm has survived, but thanks to contemporary advertisements and family records, we have some idea about the products of the firm from the late 1850's onwards. A series of advertisements appearing in the 'Engineer' in the year 1862 is reproduced. It will be noted that the firm's address is given as Berkeley Street and Granville Street. The art work is quite simple but well executed and the list of products offered is very comprehensive being set out in full below:

"Contractors' locomotives, Portable and other Steam Engines; Steam, Wharf, Ship and Travelling Cranes; Hand, Wharf, Travelling, Derrick and other Cranes; Steam and Hand Crab Winches; Travelling Crabs for Gantry Frames; Pulley Blocks etc.

Lathes; Planing, Slotting, Drilling, Screwing, Punching and Shearing Machines; Ratchet Braces and General Machinery; Wrought Iron Smiths' Hearths, Anvils, Vices etc.

Lifting Jacks, viz. Traversing, Haley's, Windlass, Tripod, Bottle etc; Improved Patent Wrought Iron Hydraulic Jacks to raise from 4 to 200 tons; Hydraulic Machines to Test Bar Iron, Steel, Chain Cables, and Small Portable for Girders and Wire. Railway Train Bell Signal Apparatus; Rail-setting Presses, Jim Crows, and other Contractors' Tools; Railway Buffers, Screw Couplings, Bolts and Nuts etc."

By 1865 the company's advertisements in the same journal give a Berkeley Street address only and are much simpler affairs with no art work.

Family records provide a list of some products between 1858 and 1864 and this is reproduced at Appendix IV. Railway wagons clearly formed a substantial part of the firm's output at this time. Fifty were built for the Vale of Neath Railway to Brunel's broad gauge in 1859 at a cost of £88.10.4½ (£88.52p) per wagon delivered to the Company. The railway company paid, it is thought, £95 each, a very small profit margin for the manufacturer.

Thomas' activities were by no means confined to the home market. Thus in 1858 four 'treble purchase crabs' (cranes) to lift 25 tons were

Another advertisement from *The Engineer* of the same period.

supplied to the Bombay, Baroda and Central India Railway. A further ten to lift 20 tons and six more to lift 15 tons were supplied to the same customer that year, and in 1859 four more to lift eight tons were provided. Nor was the export effort restricted to the 'soft' markets of the Empire. In November 1856, according to surviving family letters he was in Sweden almost certainly on business having left his wife Ann convalescing at Brighton.

In addition to the items listed in the schedule certain other products are known or thought to have been made. Appendix V which lists all the Worsdell family patents reveals two taken out by Thomas in addition to those of 1845 and 1855. In 1849 a series of machines for "automating and making continuous the manufacture of envelopes, cases etc" brought technology to the previously entirely manual process of cutting, gumming, creasing and cementing envelopes and cardboard boxes and cases. Thomas' designs were soon purchased by the De La Rue company, still a famous name in the manufacture of paper products and machinery, and it is uncertain whether Thomas himself made such equipment beyond the prototype stage.

47

In 1864 Thomas, once more in sole charge of the firm, patented an improved pulley which also formed an important part of the factory's output. Other products included pile drivers, an early steam roller for Calcutta and at least two locomotives.

Thomas employed a number of people in his business who were later to distinguish themselves in engineering. Several members of the talented Tangye family, Cornish Quakers, held responsible posts at his works. The first was Richard who arrived in Birmingham in December 1852 and took up a post as clerk at £50 per year. By 1855, when William Evans was taken into partnership by Thomas, three further Tangye brothers were working for the firm. James was foreman of the works, Joseph was responsible for the development of a hydraulics manufacturing department and George was clerk of the works. This was probably the most successful period in the history of Thomas' works and the injection of Evans' capital should have given rise to further success. Alas this was not to be. Both Worsdell family papers and Sir Richard Tangye's biography suggest that the period of

The Tangye brothers, Cornish Quakers who worked at Thomas Worsdell's Birmingham Works before founding their own company at the nearby Cornwall Works.

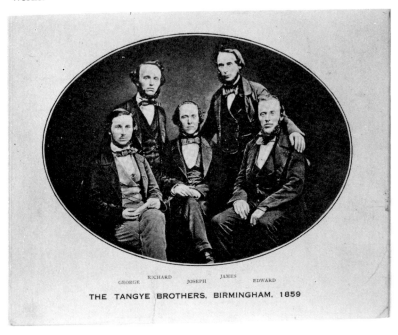

GEORGE   RICHARD   JOSEPH   JAMES   EDWARD

THE TANGYE BROTHERS, BIRMINGHAM, 1859

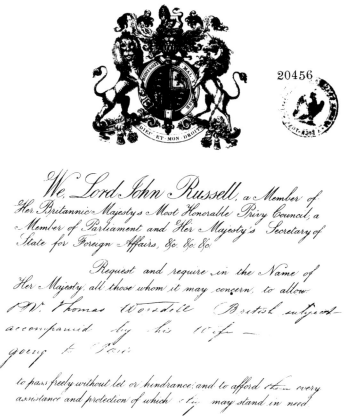

20456

We, Lord John Russell, a Member of Her Britannic Majesty's Most Honorable Privy Council, a Member of Parliament and Her Majesty's Secretary of State for Foreign Affairs, &c. &c. &c.

Request and require in the Name of Her Majesty, all those whom it may concern, to allow Mr. Thomas Worsdell British subject accompanied by his Wife —

going to Paris

to pass freely without let or hindrance; and to afford them every assistance and protection of which they may stand in need.

Given at the Foreign Office, London, the day of June 1860

Russell

Signature of the Bearer.

Thomas Worsdell's passport for a trip to Paris with his wife, issued 16th June 1860.

Thomas' partnership with Evans was a disastrous one. The trouble arose over a very trivial matter. Whereas Richard had been trusted absolutely by Thomas, Evans insisted on there being a window in the partition which divided their offices and that there should be a curtain on his (Evans') side of the window. Richard, only 22 and spirited, was indignant and when Evans refused to back down he resigned. Within a short period his three brothers also left Worsdell and Evans and in 1860 in conjunction with a fifth brother, Edward, set up their own engineering business at the Cornwall Works nearby. Evans was thus held responsible for 'driving away' the gifted Tangye brothers, a blow from which the firm probably never fully recovered.

It cannot be emphasised too strongly that Richard Tangye's argument was solely with William Evans. He remained on terms of great friendship with Thomas for the remainder of the latter's life, some 40 years. In later years Thomas took pride in the fact of having brought the Tangyes to Birmingham and kept a portrait of Richard in his house. Once on a visit to the Cornwall Works with his gardener from Ulverston Thomas was heard to remark "Tangyes make steam engines as fast as you can grow daisies". Richard Tangye certainly reciprocated Thomas' feelings of regard, publicly expressing his gratitude to his first and only employer.

Thomas' nephew William Worsdell (1838-1916) had two periods of employment with the firm. He served an apprenticeship here from 1855 to 1859 unusually being appointed a foreman whilst still under indentures. The young man's rapid advancement being presumably not unconnected with the departure of the Tangye brothers. After a two year break he returned to the Birmingham works at the age of 23 as manager, a post he held for about four years. By 1862, however, the partnership with Evans had been dissolved so William Worsdell's disillusionment with the firm which resulted in his departure in 1865, could not be laid at that gentleman's door.

Thomas' interest in the firm seems to have diminished after his nephew's departure and he retired from the business in 1867 at the early age of 49 to live at Dykelands, Three Bridges, near Ulverston. Always a devout Quaker Thomas was attracted to the Morecambe Bay area by both its religious and family associations and spent the remainder of his life there until his death on 27th March 1893. His wife Ann survived him by ten years, dying at Ulverston on 22nd April 1903, leaving an estate valued in excess of £30,000 gross, a considerable sum of money for the time. She made bequests to various charitable causes in Ulverston and her home town of Lancaster. Quaker charities also featured prominently in her will and it is significant to note in view of her father-in-law Thomas Clarke Worsdell's interests that £300 was bequeathed to Birmingham Homeopathic Hospital.

George, Thomas Clarke Worsdell II's youngest son, was born on 21st May 1821 at Preston and was also destined to make his reputation in business founding an engineering works which only closed its doors in the 1980's after some 135 years of trading.

George was given a Quaker education under Mr George Edmondson near Blackburn. After a period of training with his father at Crown Street he journeyed to Leipzig with the family in 1837. He must have gained useful railway and engineering skills from that experience and upon his return to England in 1838 he avidly sought to acquire further knowledge working in London at Euston, then at New Cross (possibly on the London and Croydon Railway) and later at Swindon, where for a few months he served under Sir Daniel Gooch of the Great Western Railway. Interestingly this must have been during the period of the construction of the locomotive works which was authorised by the Directors of the company in October 1840 but not brought into regular use until January 1843, by which time

Thomas Worsdell in later life.

51

George was engaged upon locomotive work at Hull having completed a few months study in London under a 'well known civil engineer'. History does not recall the identity of this engineer but I. K. Brunel and Robert Stephenson must be possible contenders.

At Hull George also had the task of repairing the engines of the 'Sirius' a vessel of 700 tons owned by James Beale, a Quaker, and others. In 1838 this ship had accomplished the first crossing of the Atlantic Ocean made under steam, the journey from London to New York taking twenty five days. The 'Sirius' arrived in New York a few hours ahead of the S.S. 'Great Western' which crossed from Bristol in fifteen days. George would have been reunited with his father and mother in Hull for they settled in that city by about 1841.

By 1845 George had acquired a wealth of engineering experience and sought to start his own railway equipment manufacturing firm. He chose Warrington as the location for the embryonic business. At this time a small town with little in the way of industry, Warrington had lost its role as a coaching centre with the coming of the railway, but was very well situated midway between Liverpool and Manchester. George acquired an old bone-fertilizer works and transformed it into the Dallam Forge. There he rolled the first bar of iron to be produced in Warrington (and indeed Lancashire) with his own hands. Such was the excellence of his products, however, that within six years George had received the medal of the Great Exhibition of 1851 "for excellence of iron and of railway plant".

In 1851 too, he married Jane, the youngest daughter of Edward Bolton of Sankey Street, Warrington and of nearby Penketh, a prominent Quaker philanthropist and businessman. Jane had received a good Quaker education under Mr Joseph Edmundson at Penketh House where the brothers John and Jacob Bright, both to become MPs, had studied. Her brother Edward was to achieve prominence in Warrington as a glass manufacturer and two more brothers Thomas and George founded the Widnes Alkali Company nearby. With a successful business and a 'good' marriage George seemed very well placed to make his fortune, but this was not to be. He was remembered as an extremely energetic, sociable and open handed young man during the early years of prosperity in his twenties and thirties but unfortunately he became victim to insomnia of a very serious kind which led to a short lived but complete breakdown of his health in 1857. The breakdown coincided with a decline in the fortunes of the Dallam Forge and although it is tempting to speculate on a 'cause and effect' mechanism it is not evident at this remove which might have been the trigger of the other.

Suffice it to say that the business failed and he was declared bankrupt. The screw was turned further when the Hardshaw East Monthly Meeting disowned him and cast him out from the Friends in 1858. We can only speculate on the heartbreak involved for George and his wife and their three small children at these events, but George proved resilient soon obtaining a post at Cammell's iron and steel works at Workington in Cumberland. After two years here, by 1860, his health had sufficiently recovered for him to take another post this time in Manchester at the great railway carriage and equipment works of John Ashbury at Openshaw. Here his talents and character were readily acknowledged and in 1861 he was appointed general manager of this very large undertaking. Again his response to the stress of high office was to worry himself into sleeplessness and ill health and he was forced to give up his post at Openshaw.

After a period of complete rest he joined his brother Thomas at the Birmingham works. Moving on again, by now restored to better health, he took over the management of the Lancaster Waggon Company in 1866. He remained here until 1872 when the insomnia and ill-health which had plagued him for so long became so acute that he was forced to retire at the age of 51. He stayed on in Lancaster serving occasionally on charitable committees and keeping abreast of engineering developments. Relieved of the pressures of high level management George appears to have thrived, living in retirement at 70 Brookfield Terrace a further forty years before dying on 1st December 1912 in his ninety-second year. His wife Jane survived to celebrate their golden wedding in 1901 and died on Christmas Day 1903 aged 83.

There were three children of the marriage, all born in Warrington before the unfortunate events of 1857/8. Edward, born on 21st March 1852, was to become a prominent Quaker teacher and writer and his life will receive consideration in the final chapter of the present work. The daughters, Clara Jane (1854-1921) and Elizabeth Ann (1856-1942) never married and moved with their parents to Lancaster in 1866, both dying there many years later.

George must have been well respected in Lancaster for it is recorded that the Lancaster Friends reinstated him as a member making some amends for the harsh treatment meted out to him by the Hardshaw East Meeting years before. The reinstatement was carried out without his knowledge recognising that as a man of some pride he would never apply for readmission of his own volition.

The business that George founded, the Dallam Forge, grew and prospered throughout his life and long after it. After the failure of the business in 1857 the firm became Neild and Company, the partners being William Neild, Henry Bleckly and Thomas Fell. The Worsdells certainly had Neild relatives so it seems probable that the takeover was a fairly 'near to home' affair. In 1865 a private limited company, the Dallam Forge Company, was formed, the principals being the same gentlemen plus Edward Beck. The new company was successful from the outset manufacturing bar iron, railway axles and tyres and iron plate. Much of the output was exported through Liverpool. During the same period Henry Bleckly and his sons joined with members of the Rylands family to form the Warrington Wire Iron Company Ltd in order to supply the town's famous wire trade with its raw material, wire rods, which had previously been brought in from Staffordshire and Shropshire.

In 1874 the Dallam Forge Company and the Warrington Wire Iron Company were amalgamated with the Pearson and Knowles collieries of Wigan to form the Pearson and Knowles Coal and Iron Company Ltd. The enterprise continued to grow with the absorption of the Rylands Brothers wire business at Warrington and the Moss Hall and Wigan Junction Collieries at Wigan in the early years of the twentieth century.

The Dallam Forge was turning out between 1,000 and 1,250 tons of finished iron and steel bars per week by 1908. Large tonnages of hoops, iron and steel sheets and wire rods were also produced. A wide range of engineering products were made at this time including railway wheels and axles (forged on a 2,000 ton hydraulic press), constructional iron and steel work for bridges, cranes and gantries, blast furnaces, calcining kilns, colliery haulage gear and winding engines, pit head frames, patent bye-product coke oven installations, gas producer plant, hot metal and slag ladles and steel works plant of all kinds as well as iron and brass castings of every sort. Amongst Dallam's most impressive products were a 200 foot span bridge over the River Dee for the Wrexham and Ellesmere Railway and a 225 foot span bridge for the Liverpool Overhead Railway.

In May 1930 the Pearson and Knowles Company was one of the constituents of the Lancashire Steel Company, formed to rationalise production at that time of recession. The new combine was a very large enterprise which operated a vast steel making plant at Irlam, to the west of Manchester and eight miles from Warrington. Originally built by the Partington Iron and Steel Company, Irlam was to become part of the British Steel Corporation after nationalisation, steelmaking finally ceasing in the 1970s.

The Dallam Forge however outlived the demise of steelmaking at Irlam becoming finally known as the Bewsey Road Mills of the British Steel

George Worsdell (1821-1912), the founder of the Dallam Forge at Warrington. This historic photograph shows him in the garden of his late brother Thomas' house, Dykelands at Ulverston, in November 1896. Thomas Worsdell's prize-winning model coach 'The Experience' (illustrated) was sent to the London and North Western Railway Museum at Euston, in the following month, by George and Thomas' widow Ann.

Corporation's Scunthorpe division. The furnaces were damped down for the last time on 18th July 1980 and 680 steel workers became redundant. Writing to the *Warrington Guardian* in 1981 after the closure Dr Johnson Ball of Stourbridge, Worcestershire, recalled starting an engineering apprenticeship at Dallam, by then in 'P and K' ownership, in October 1915. At this time the works was given over to the wartime production of shells using existing plant hastily adapted for the new role pending the commissioning of purpose built munitions factories. In this way Dallam made an invaluable contribution to the war effort but with the coming of peace the economic depression and industrial troubles of the 1920s led to decline and redundancies and the eventual amalgamations of 1930.

Clearance of the Bewsey Road site in early 1985 released a 26 acre site for redevelopment for various industrial users. Amongst the new tenants found for the site were Sterling Cables and the brewers, Tetley Walker. The contractors clearing the site found evidence of apparently three generations of buildings there and at the north end the remains of what appeared to be a pottery works, presumably associated with the bone mill purchased by George Worsdell in 1845. Amongst other interesting finds were five wells, a clay pit and many culverts and flues. The concrete floor supporting the rolling mills was found to be up to thirty feet thick.

Whilst it is encouraging that new users for the old Dallam Forge site were found so readily, it is unfortunate that the works that George Worsdell founded have been totally obliterated, particularly as for so long the Pearson and Knowles Company was by far the largest employer in Warrington; as many as 4,500 men in the town worked at 'P & K' in the early years of this century. The area owed much of its prosperity at that time to the foresight and enterprise of the 24 years old George Worsdell in the middle years of the 19th century. It was he who presided over the initial establishment of the Forge in an area not previously involved in iron and steel making. Engineering skills were to be had locally but not experience in iron making, then chiefly centred on South Wales, Yorkshire, Staffordshire and Shropshire. George would have had to import men of the right calibre as well as materials and it is a tribute to his judgment that the enterprise grew so quickly and achieved the reputation for quality of output recognised at the Great Exhibition.

Just before the start of work on this biography iron and steel production in Warrington sadly came to an end with the closure of the Monks, Hall works of British Steel's Scunthorpe division early in 1986.

V

THE LOCOMOTIVE ENGINEERS

(i) T. W. Worsdell

Two of Nathaniel Worsdell's sons, Thomas William (known in the family as William) and Wilson, were to achieve eminence as railway engineers and locomotive designers.

Thomas William Worsdell was born on 14th January 1838 at 17 Laurel Street, Liverpool, the home of his parents. He was sent to school at the early age of two years being placed in the charge of Abraham Isherwood. At four he moved to Crewe on his father's appointment there as manager of the coachmaking department. At Crewe he was educated at first by the Misses Reed and later by Mr Cross, a Presbyterian Minister. William recalled in later life the aptness of this gentleman's surname. In 1847 he was sent to Ackworth School in Yorkshire as a boarder. He remained at this Quaker foundation until 1852 when he returned to Crewe working for six months in his father's office and timber yard for the London and North Western Railway. At the beginning of 1853 he went to Queenwood College, at Stockbridge in Hampshire, a converted Owenite colony. He spent only a year here, however, returning home to serve a year long apprenticeship at the Crewe timber yard.

Happily two interesting mementoes of William's schooldays have survived. A letter dated 19th December 1844, a few weeks before his seventh birthday, to his parents shows the young scholar to have had a very fine hand indeed. From a later period the account sent by Queenwood College to his father Nathaniel covering William's first six months there makes interesting reading. Headmaster George Edmondson's invoice itemises expenses in great detail with separate entries for tailoring, shoemaking, medical attendance, drawing materials, use of musical instruments, haircutting etc. A half year's board and instruction cost £25.

Early in 1855 William went as an apprentice to his uncle Thomas Worsdell's Berkeley Street engineering works in Birmingham. Before completing his apprenticeship and at the age of only twenty he was appointed a foreman. Unfortunately as in the case of his uncle George at the Dallam Forge, the long hours and heavy responsibility of the job took its toll. After a serious illness he went back to the LNWR at Crewe and obtained a position in the locomotive department drawing office under John Ramsbottom, the then Locomotive Superintendent.

Two years later in 1861 he returned to Birmingham to take over as manager of Thomas Worsdell's works. He remained here almost five years before the rift occurred which led to his leaving the company. The details are not known but it would seem that in some way William was aggrieved that an agreement entered into when he rejoined the firm was not adhered to by the 'company', which presumably by this date meant his uncle Thomas, the latter's one-time partner Mr Evans having already moved on.

T. W. (William) Worsdell and Mary Ann Worsdell at about the time of their marriage in 1865.

William emigrated to the United States in the second half of 1865. Perhaps predictably he chose to settle in the Quaker state of Pennsylvania entering the service of the Pennsylvania Railroad (PRR) as a mechanic. He was appointed Master Mechanic in 1868 and given charge of the Altoona workshops. At Altoona he was thus responsible for the construction of locomotives, carriages, machinery and structural iron work such as bridges. He was notable for introducing locomotive fireboxes of steel rather than copper on the PRR and with considerable success. Interestingly British steel fireboxes of that period, being of a different design consisting of a single plate of the metal, were very prone to failure. William was to remain a proponent of the innovative use of cast steel components in his later careers in Britain at Crewe and Stratford. Little is known about his stay in Pennsylvania save that he spent more than six years there and during that time fathered three children by his wife Mary Ann (née Batt) whom he had married on 29th June 1865 at the Friends' Meeting House, Yealand Conyers, Lancashire.

The house in Altoona, Pennsylvania, where William and Mary Ann Worsdell lived. Their children Mary Isabella, Wilson Crosfield and Henry were born here.

An undated fragment of one letter from William to his father Nathaniel has, however, survived from this period. It can be attributed with certainty to 1866 since in it William expresses much concern at the 'sad conduct' of his brother Edwin in marrying Elizabeth Gray, which occurred in that year, and also speaks of his brother Wilson at Ackworth School, which the latter left towards the end of the same year. Much of the letter is concerned with locomotive matters and contains two delightful pen and ink sketches of engines: the first illustrates a typical American 4-4-0 of the period whilst the second depicts a handsome saddle tank locomotive of the 2-6-2 wheel arrangement which he had designed with the approval of the company's Engineer. It must have been quite a large machine being over 30 feet between the centres of the outer wheels and 40 feet long overall. Coupled wheels were 5ft. 6ins. in diameter and 'all the wheels except the driving wheel are made to turn a little so as to accommodate the curves'. The saddle tank carried 2,000 gallons of water and the coal bunkers 2¼ tons. William was also engaged in 'designing a small engine and car for the directors to inspect the line in'.

Two delightful sketches of Pennsylvania Railroad locomotives contained in a letter sent from Altoona to his father Nathaniel by William Worsdell in 1866.

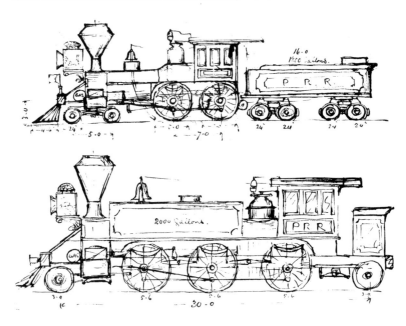

He provided a detailed description of both the design features and livery of a typical PRR 4-4-0 locomotive. Significantly for his future designs in England he was most taken with the driver's cab provided. 'Each engine has a complete little house, 8 feet square and 7 feet high, for the enginemen with doors and windows which can all be laid open during summer'. He was, as later, much exercised by aesthetics and thought the Altoona engines 'painted most fantastically....it makes them look very inferior to our finished engines, gilt is used lavishly, they don't seem to think that gold leaf costs anything'. Chimneys were black, boiler barrels slate blue, domes polished brass, sandboxes green and gold, cabs polished walnut with gilt lining, cylinders blue, framing dark green, wheel splashers emerald green and wheels vermilion and gilt.

William described the United States thus: 'It is a capital place for practice here as we have so many different kinds of railroad' and expressed the wish that his brother Wilson would be able to come out and join him and his wife Mary. The Quaker community of the State of Pennsylvania was closely associated with the management of the railroad which had been established in 1846. John Edgar Thomson (1808-74), and of Quaker stock, was the line's dynamic first Chief Engineer. He was to devote the rest of his life to the successful development of the company. The Roberts family, originally Welsh Quakers who had purchased land outside Philadelphia in the 17th century and became farmers, maltsters and ironmongers were major shareholders. George Brooke Roberts (1833-97) was to become president of the railroad and to have a grand-daughter and great grand-daughter who married Rockefellers.

Interestingly we can surmise that on the PRR lineside fires caused by locomotives were a problem that exercised William, for on 22nd June 1871 a specification was lodged at the Patent Office, London by John Henry Johnson, of 47 Lincoln's Inn Fields, on behalf of James Smith and Thomas William Worsdell, of "Altoona, County of Blair, State of Pennsylvania, U.S.A." A patent was granted for the invention of "Improvements in Spark Arrestors" in the words of the applicants "an invention particularly applicable to locomotive engine boilers but also to portable and other engines wherein a steam blast is employed". As we shall see later, it was to be the first of several patents taken out by William in the course of his career. A list of all Worsdell family patents is presented in Appendix V.

That William returned at all to England is largely due to the redoubtable Francis William Webb, Locomotive Superintendent of the LNWR at Crewe from 1871 to 1903. William applied for the post of Works Manager at Crewe in June 1871 but any appointment was held over until Webb had succeeded Ramsbottom as Superintendent. Webb visited William in Pennsylvania at about this time and we must conclude that the latter was what we should now call 'headhunted' by Webb. William returned to England in August 1871 but was not confirmed in post until 11th October when Webb was firmly in control.

William's tenure at Crewe lasted ten years and saw considerable improvements in the facilities there. In particular the company erected its own furnaces for the production of steel. This had been occasioned by the developments over the previous ten to twelve years under Ramsbottom, who with Webb as Chief Draughtsman, had greatly improved the locomotive department. With the object of reducing costs new methods and materials were introduced amounting almost to mass production techniques and making Crewe the most cost effective works in Britain. Indeed the expansion of capacity was such that the output of new locomotives increased from 100 in 1864 to 138 by 1874. The company used some of this capacity to embark on construction not merely for its own use, but for other companies also. Most notably 101 engines of three different types were built for the Lancashire and Yorkshire Railway Company between 1871 and 1874. Independent locomotive building firms objected strongly to the LNWR setting themselves up as contractors in this way considering the action to be beyond the legitimate activities of a railway company. The firms, forming themselves into the Locomotive Manufacturers Association, were successful in obtaining an injunction preventing Crewe from indulging in such activities.

It seems quite clear that William's association with Webb at Crewe intensified his interest in compound locomotives, that is those in which steam is used twice, first in a high pressure cylinder and then again as the exhaust from the first cylinder passes to a lower pressure cylinder. Webb produced his first compound engine in 1879 having been inspired by the Mallet compound locomotive for the Bayonne and Biarritz Railway which was exhibited at the Paris Exhibition of 1878. Webb's compound locomotive was a rebuild of an old orthodox locomotive, the 'Medusa', with one cylinder reduced in size to act with high pressure steam the other unchanged to work at lower pressure. The resultant two cylinder compound was a configuration that William Worsdell was to favour in his later designs, although Webb subsequently became absorbed by the three cylinder format, two operating at high pressure and one at low pressure. Though not an unqualified success compound engines were to form the mainstay of the LNWR's express passenger engines for the remainder of the Webb era.

William had started at Crewe in 1871 at a salary of £600 per annum. His qualities were such that by the end of 1876 he was being paid £800. As a typical Quaker he was, too, immersing himself in the affairs of the town. To some extent of course this would be expected of a senior LNWR man. His immediate superior Francis Webb, for example, was a town councillor and Mayor of the town in 1886/7, a county councillor and prime mover in the foundation of the Memorial Cottage Hospital, a sorely needed facility which opened in 1895. William also involved himself in local government as his father Nathaniel had before him. He became a member of the Local Board of Health in 1873, was elected its Chairman in 1874-5 and served on it until its replacement by the new Town Council in June 1877. Defeated in the first elections to the Council he secured a place on it in November of the same year winning 672 votes in the East Ward with the help of Liberal support and joining Nathaniel who had re-entered local politics at this time after a lengthy break. William was re-elected unopposed as an Independent in 1880 and became a Justice of the Peace. Quite naturally he fulfilled the

T. W. (William) Worsdell (1838-1916), of the London and North Western, Pennsylvania, Great Eastern and North Eastern Railways.

role of vice-president of the Mechanics Institution (under Webb's presidency) from 1872 to 1881, again following his father's example.

William in harness with Webb presided over a period of solid achievement at Crewe although there was one great problem for him. As an ambitious man he would have realised that the opportunity for advancement at Crewe was virtually non existent. He was 37 years old by 1875 but only two years younger than his Superintendent, Webb, who was at the height of his powers. Clearly he would have to move to secure a superintendent's post. In October 1875 he applied for such a position with the Lancashire and Yorkshire Railway but, although short listed, was not successful, W. Barton Wright being appointed. His chance came in August 1881 when Massey Bromley resigned as Locomotive Superintendent of the Great Eastern Railway (GER) at Stratford Works, East London, entering private practice as a consulting engineer. William was appointed Superintendent that November and moved with his family to East London. That he was greatly respected at Crewe is born out by the

Solid Victorian family residences at Crewe. In the late 1870s William Worsdell and his family lived at Deva Villa, on the left, and his father Nathaniel next door to the right.

following letter published anonymously in the *Crewe Guardian* of 3rd December 1881:

HONOUR TO WHOM HONOUR IS DUE
TO THE EDITOR OF THE GUARDIAN

Sir, Looking through your issue of the 22nd inst., I see we are about losing from Crewe a most worthy and beneficial townsman, one whom we shall not be able every day to replace. Looking back at his past services I think my fellow-townsmen will agree with me that the firm, true and unflinching manner in which he has carried out, all and every one of the several works, both municipal and magisterial, which has fallen to his duty to perform, deserves the highest credit. As townsmen possessing the best amount of gratitude, we are duty bound to express the regret we shall feel in losing so high and estimable a gentleman, yet we should be wantonly ungrateful if we did not feel great pleasure at the high and providential call which takes our worthy townsman from among us. Therefore, I trust there will be an expression of esteem on the part of the inhabitants of the town generally and that all with one accord will unanimously come forward and respond to the appeal of the committee who are bringing forward a scheme for a testimonial, by way of a parting expression of heartfelt gratitude. I, for one, think the matter ought not to be left to the company's employees but should be unanimously taken up by every burgess.
Yours truly,
AN OBSERVER OF TRUE CHARACTER

It is also fortunate that two mementoes of this period have survived in the Worsdell family papers. The first is a letter from Mr S. Reay, the secretary of the LNWR at its Euston Headquarters, written on behalf of the directors of the company accepting William's resignation, thanking him for his efforts and congratulating him on his 'important' appointment. It is dated 18th November 1881. A similar letter dated 9th December from Frederick Cooke, the Town Clerk of Crewe, to William on the occasion of his resignation from the Town Council has also survived. His fellow councillors wished William 'every prosperity, health and happiness' and generously remitted the fine imposed by the Municipal Acts upon members resigning their seats.

Before their move, William and Mary Worsdell had been living at Deva Villa, Crewe next door to William's father Nathaniel. Their family was complete by this time. Three children had been born in Pennsylvania, Mary Isabella (1866), Wilson Crosfield (1867) and Henry (1869). Mary died at the age of four but three further children were born at Crewe after the return to England in 1871. They were Robert (1873), Archibald (1874) and finally, Ronald (1881). The lives of four of these five sons will be touched upon in the final chapter.

Despite the move south, William had, like his father Nathaniel and uncles Thomas and George before him, made a commitment to the Furness and Morecambe Bay area with its strong Quaker connections and where he had met and married Mary Batt. In 1879 he had bought some land at Arnside, Westmorland and built a residence there named 'Stonycroft'.

A fine portrait of William and Mary Ann Worsdell and their five sons taken about 1888. (Left to right, Archie, Henry, Mary Ann, Wilson Crosfield, Ronald, William, Robert).

Both house and garden were designed by William himself. The family used 'Stonycroft' initially as a holiday home and they lived there permanently after William's retirement in 1890.

In London he brought the same drive and determination to his duties at Stratford that he had demonstrated at Crewe. The Great Eastern was a relatively small railway which had been formed in 1862 from the amalgamation of a number of smaller companies in East Anglia and South Eastern England, north of the Thames. The works at Stratford had been established in 1847 by the Eastern Counties Railway but in its early years this and the later Great Eastern company obtained its engines largely from outside contractors. With the appointment of Massey Bromley as works manager in 1874 under William Adams, the facilities at Stratford were reorganised and expanded allowing an increased number of locomotives to be repaired annually and making possible more in-house new locomotive construction. The succession of Bromley to the Superintendent's post in February 1878 resulted in a greater proportion of GER locomotives being constructed by the company themselves at Stratford than ever before. William Worsdell went even further. He decreed on taking office in February 1882 that in future all locomotives required by the railway should be produced at Stratford, and apart from some goods engines urgently required for the opening of the Great Northern and Great Eastern Joint Railway in 1882 this policy was adhered to.

As Locomotive Superintendent William carried overall responsibility not just for the day to day running of Stratford Works through the Works Manager but also for all aspects of locomotive design. Upon appointment he set in hand the design and construction of a series of locomotive types to meet the requirements of the expanding company. In producing these he not only provided locomotives strikingly different in appearance from those of his predecessors, thus establishing a new 'house style' on the Great Eastern, but also laid the design foundations for his later and very handsome engines constructed at Gateshead and Darlington for the North Eastern Railway. It has been observed that it might have been expected that in these first designs for the GER some of the influence of his six years on the Pennsylvania Railroad would have been apparent. Indeed his predecessor Bromley had also visited America to investigate construction methods there and on his return had been responsible for many American features in Adams' and later his own designs, most notably in the fifteen locomotives of the 'mogul' type built in 1878-79 for coal traffic. However, William's work betrayed little American influence owing more to the Crewe tradition. In his short tenure at Stratford five different classes of locomotive were designed and built. Summary information concerning these types is presented in Appendix 1. His first design was an express passenger locomotive of the 2-4-0 wheel arrangement with 7ft. driving wheels and 18ins. diameter cylinders. Designated the 'G14' class, the engines incorporated features redolent of Crewe and others which were to become something of a personal trademark. Falling into both categories was the Joy valve gear used by Webb at Crewe in the period when William was works manager there and extensively thereafter by Webb and by George Whale and C .J. Bowen Cooke, his successors as Chief Mechanical Engineer.

The Lancashire and Yorkshire Railway also employed Joy valve gear almost exclusively, but it did not find favour elsewhere except in William Worsdell's designs for the Great Eastern and North Eastern Railways where it was ever present until removed by William's successors on both railways. The valve gear was usually employed on William's engines driving flat valves above the cylinders, a very convenient arrangement. Other Crewe inspired features were the radial axle boxes of the Webb type on the leading wheels and Ramsbottom safety valves. The 'G14s' sported the elegant continuous long splashers covering both pairs of driving wheels which were to become such a feature of William's express passenger engines. The one concession to American practise comprised the Westinghouse air brake, the ugly donkey pump of which was hidden behind the wheel splashers. William retained the tapered stovepipe chimney which had become a familiar Great Eastern feature and introduced a comfortable and elegant cab with curved side sheets in his first design. As well as being a characteristic feature of Stratford locomotives for many years, the provision of a comfortable working environment for footplate staff was also something central to William Worsdell's design approach both at Stratford and Gateshead and probably owed much to both his Quakerism and his American experience.

The 'G14s' were anticipated with much excitement and it is recalled that on pay nights (Fridays) before the emergence of the first member of the class, No. 562, from the workshops local shopkeepers and hawkers were selling 'G14' books, toffee and even rock containing an impression of the locomotive in cross section. When the locomotive finally appeared to everyone's pleasure it was finished with highly decorative brass mountings, a feature absent from Stratford locomotives from the time of William Adams' austere rule. On the morning after its emergence No. 562 was steamed and run up to Snaresbrook to fetch William from his home and bring him to Stratford.

Photographs of T. W. Worsdell's first design for the Great Eastern Railway are not easy to obtain and this view of 'G14' No. 0562 is not of the highest quality. It shows the prototype as rebuilt, with the distinctive continuous splasher over the driving wheels removed exposing the air brake pump.

(Great Eastern Railway Society)

In service the 'G14s' proved something of a disappointment never being renowned as fast, free running machines. Twenty were built in 1882-83 but from the outset there were problems with the Joy valve gear resulting from the fracture of iron castings. The valve gear too was blamed for the heavy coal consumption of the engines. The prototype locomotive was after a few years, rebuilt with Stephenson valve gear and with individual splashers over the driving wheels exposing the air brake pump in the process. Even despite the rebuilding, however, the 'G14s' were not destined for a long life, scrapping commencing in 1895 and the last survivor being taken out of service by 1901.

William's second design was a goods engine of the 0-6-0 wheel arrangement classified 'Y14'. Fifty were constructed at Stratford between 1883 and 1886 and were so successful that they remained the standard GER freight engine for the remainder of the century. They were eventually superseded on the heaviest freight workings by larger locomotives but a measure of their worth can be gained from the fact that no less than 289 engines of the class were built in all over a period of thirty years by four different superintendents. Forty five of them were used by the Royal Engineers' Railway Operating Division in France during World War I. They proved very popular machines and presumably because of their light axle loading, were used nearer to the front lines than any other of the British main line engines used in that theatre of war.

T. W. Worsdell's most famous engines for the Great Eastern the 'Y14' six-wheelers of 1883 were constructed over a period of 30 years and were still running in the 1950s. Number 681 was built in 1885 whilst William was still in charge at Stratford Works. *(North Woolwich Old Station Museum)*

After the grouping of 1923 when the Great Eastern became part of the London and North Eastern Railway (LNER) the 'Y14s' became reclassified as 'J15s' and many survived to become part of the British Railways fleet on nationalisation in 1948 though by now relegated to branch line and light duties and sometimes much rebuilt. As many as 50 of the original 289 lasted until the late 1950s and happily one, No. 564 built in 1912, has survived preserved in working order on the North Norfolk Railway at Sheringham.

A very attractive shot of a 'Y14' on passenger work in LNER days. Number 7640, built in 1899, is seen on Brentwood bank on a down Southend train.

(J. Carrier collection/ NRM, York)

Another design appeared in 1883 from the Stratford drawing office. This was for the first 'tram' engines to be owned by the company, small four-wheeled locomotives designed to run through public streets and, to conform with Board of Trade safety requirements, completely 'boxed in' so that no moving parts were exposed. They were also fitted with cowcatchers, warning bells and governors which prevented speeds in excess of 8mph. Initially three engines of class 'G15' were built to work on the five miles long Wisbech and Upwell Tramway which ran on or alongside public roads for much of its course. Later examples of the type hauled trains over the tramway from Yarmouth station to the docks.

A delightful view of a passenger train about to leave Upwell for Wisbech in March 1923. Locomotive No. 132 was one of the original three 'G15's built in 1883.

Potter collection/NRM, York)

After this eccentric diversion William returned to the mainstream of locomotive design with the introduction in 1884 of the 'M15' class of tank engines with the 2-4-2 wheel arrangement. Intended for suburban and branch line passenger work they were powerful engines and incorporated Joy valve gear and the Westinghouse brake. These engines earned a

The enclosed 'G15' tram engines were constructed for running alongside public roads on the Upwell Tramway in LNER days. *(North Woolwich Old Station Museum)*

reputation for excessive coal consumption which resulted in the nickname 'Gobblers' but must have been considered a success because further engines of a very similar design were constructed by William's successor James Holden, also a Quaker, between 1886 and 1909 making a total of 160 in all. Yet more of a slightly modified design were constructed from 1911 onwards by the then superintendent Stephen Holden. Again these engines were remarkably long lived even some of the original Worsdell/James Holden type surviving until the 1950s.

William's early experience with compound locomotives whilst working under Francis Webb at Crewe has already been alluded to. They were to become a persisting fascination for him. His final design at Stratford was a compound locomotive of the 4-4-0 wheel arrangement based on the two cylinder Von Borries system. Eleven 'G16s' were built in all, No. 230 the prototype in 1884 and the remainder in 1885. These engines at first glance bore some similarities with the earlier 'G14' design, the boilers being identical and driving wheels of 7ft. diameter being again used. Between the frames, however, the layout was very different, the left hand (high pressure) cylinder having a diameter of 18ins. whilst the right hand (low pressure) cylinder measured 26ins. across, the latter being so large that part of the frame of the engine had to be cut away to accommodate it. The Joy valve gear was again employed.

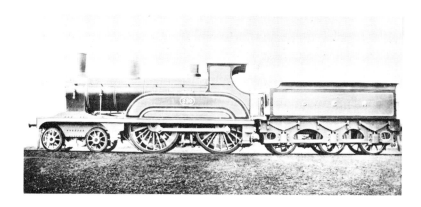

The 'G16' compound 4-4-0 No. 230 as built. This was T. W. Worsdell's last design for the GER. The graceful splasher covering the driving wheels and hiding the unsightly air brake pump was a characteristic feature on later North Eastern Railway engines. The contrast with the rebuilt 'G14' previously illustrated is very marked. *(By courtesy of the National Railway Museum, York)*

These compound engines appear to have been reasonably, if not spectacularly, successful and details have survived of some quite creditable work performed on the Liverpool Street to Cambridge and Colchester lines. In 1892 however William's successor at Stratford, James Holden, rebuilt all eleven engines as orthodox locomotives with two high pressure cylinders of 18in. diameter. This decision may not be an indication of any intrinsic fault with the compound locomotives as built but might rather reflect the strong prejudices, both for and against, that compounding provoked in the early days. Whatever the reason these engines were not long lived even in their rebuilt form, all being scrapped by 1904.

William's commitment to the compound locomotive was to be a long one which was continued in his next position on the North 'Eastern Railway at Gateshead, but it was at Stratford that he first sought to improve on the work of others in his compound design. Perhaps this might be the place to embark on a short technical discussion about compound locomotives. The advantage of the compounding lies in its inherent fuel economy, the steam being used twice first in a high pressure cylinder and then in a low pressure cylinder before exhausting to the atmosphere via the chimney. Quite substantial savings could be made. For example, James Holden calculated that William's compound engines showed a saving in fuel of 14% over the simple G14s when worked at a boiler pressure of 160lb although this was reduced to only 2% at a pressure of 150lb. Compound engines worked most efficiently when running at reasonable speeds but were generally considered unsuitable for work which involved much stopping and starting or where frequent starting on gradients was called for. The two cylinder compound of the Von Borries type gave rise to particular problems in this respect having only the one high pressure cylinder. If the crank happened to be at the 'dead centre' position then no traction would be obtained and the locomotive could not get started. (This is never a problem where there are two high presure cylinders, since the cranks are set at right angles to each other and the locomotive can always start in one direction or the other).

The way around this problem if the locomotive failed to start on the high pressure (HP) cylinder was to admit the steam direct to the low pressure (LP) cylinder. This steam would exert a back pressure on the HP cylinder tending to move the engine in the opposite direction to that wanted. To avoid this William employed an 'intercepting valve' in the pipe between the two cylinders which would close if the pressure on the LP side of the valve were higher than on the HP side. If the driver found he had 'dead centre' on his HP cylinder he would 'shut off' and empty his HP cylinder and then close the intercepting valve. Steam would then pass into the LP cylinder but not pass back into the HP cylinder. The engine would move off and the HP cylinder would come into use as it moved off dead centre, the pressure on the HP side of the valve would rise, eventually forcing the intercepting valve open and facilitating normal compound running.

William spent much of his career seeking to improve the operation of the two cylinder compound locomotive. On the 23rd January 1885, as his first compound locomotives were being constructed, he applied for and was granted a patent (No. 999 of 1885) for "Improvements in Compound Steam Engines". In his specification William described the action of the

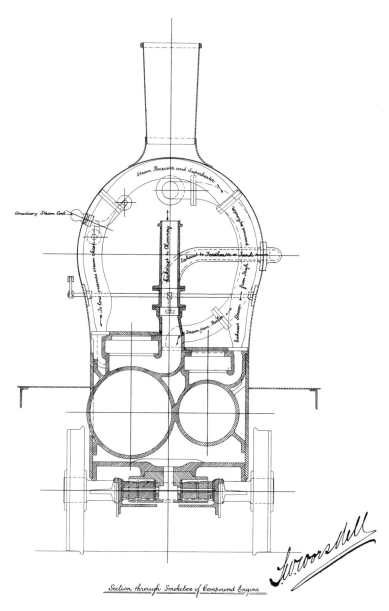

Section through Smokebox of Compound Engine

A signed drawing of a section through Smokebox of T. W. Worsdell's G16 compound 4-4-0 locomotive for the Great Eastern Railway introduced in 1884. The large (low pressure) and small (high pressure) cylinders are clearly shown.

intercepting valve outlined above. Presumably envisaging the application of the device on a wide scale he sought to protect himself (as opposed to the Great Eastern Company) by taking out the patent in his own name from his Hermon Hill address at Snaresbrook, near Wanstead in Essex.

At this stage although using the von Borries principle William appears to have been carrying out development work independently. This continued to be the case after the move to Gateshead and until his agreements with von Borries of May and July 1886 (see Appendix VII). On 29th March 1887 William described as "of Gateshead, Durham, Civil and Mechanical Engineer" lodged a specification at the Patent Office for a further improvement to the design described in the earlier patent whereby the intercepting valve would be used in conjunction with a plug cock such that exhaust steam from the high pressure cylinder would automatically open the intercepting valve and close the starting cock. William was granted a patent for this device (No. 4661 of 1887) but subsequent developments were covered by joint applications for protection by patent by William, now retired, August von Borries of Hanover and Richard Herbert Lapage of Surbiton, Surrey. Patents were granted to the three on specifications deposited on 22nd April 1892 (No. 7647), 6th April 1900 (No. 6487) and 14th December 1900 (No. 22906). All concerned the design and arrangement of valves in what has become known as the Worsdell-von Borries system of compounding. These subsequent improvements will be discussed later.

When William left Stratford in May 1885 there was no doubt that a great deal had been achieved in his brief tenure. Two of his designs were to have an extraordinary longevity on Great Eastern metals, being perpetuated by more that one successor with little modification, the highest accolade for any engineer. He will moreover always be remembered by lovers of railways, as opposed to practitioners, as the man who reintroduced the very fine royal blue colour scheme for the company's locomotives and which was to survive on the express engines right up to the First World War. This livery, complete with gold lettering and vermillion lining, bufferbeams and coupling rods is fondly remembered and fortunately can be enjoyed on some of the seven Great Eastern locomotives that have survived to the present day in preservation.

More prosaically, but also illustrating his interest in aesthetic matters, he is said to have originated the practice of displaying photographs of holiday resorts in the passenger coaches of the GER, which fashion quickly spread to other British railways.

William resigned from the Great Eastern Railway taking up the post of Locomotive Superintendent with the larger and much richer North Eastern Railway (NER) from 1st September 1885. A report of a contemporary shareholders' meeting of the Great Eastern company published in *The Railway News* of 1st August 1885 revealed one very obvious reason for William's move. The North Eastern were paying twice the salary of the southern company. "Were they (the shareholders) prepared to pay those large sums? (Cries of "No"). They must take the best they could for the money....under the circumstances they were bound to let him (William) go". The chairman described William as a 'most able and efficient engineer' and expressed pleasure that he had got such an important post with the North Eastern Railway. He went on to compliment William's work on the railway's rolling stock which was now in a "thoroughly good condition". The company owed "a debt of gratitude to Mr Worsdell, than whom there may be some as eminent, but there is no one more eminent than he in the class of work he has undertaken".

Stratford Works, East London, the engineering centre of the Great Eastern Railway, photographed in 1920. *(By courtesy of the National Railway Museum, York)*

A presentation was made to William before his departure from Stratford. This took place in the large hall of the Mechanics Institute there. A report of the event observed that in his three and a half years amongst them William's interest in the Company's employees "not only from a business point of view, but also in their social welfare, had been very marked." It had been universally agreed that some token of regard be presented. Thus it was that the meeting, chaired by Mr T. Rea supported by Mr G. Macallan, the Works Manager, and Mr Glaze, the out-door superintendent, saw the presentation of a Brinsmead piano and chiming hall-clock to the departing Superintendent. In making the presentation Mr Rea made special mention of William's courage in arriving at Stratford to take command "not as many would have done, with a lot of assistants, but he came alone."

Mr John Harrison, supporting Mr Rea, said that all could see the great improvements that had been made and also that the work had been 'kept at home'. More machinery had been placed in the works, additional men had been employed and the works had been extended. William had clearly helped much with the development of the Mechanics Institute itself. "By his help and influence new rooms had been built and furnished, and in the coming winter they would be able to have additional classes". Above all "in Mr Worsdell they saw a man who acted fairly betwen man and master—which was saying a great deal—and further, he was a Christian gentleman".

It is reported that William was received with 'ringing cheers' when he spoke in thanks. Referring to Mr Rea's remark about his coming to Stratford alone without assistants, he expressed the view that it was only right for him to see if there were men in post at Stratford who could carry out his programmes before he thought of employing strangers. In this he had been proved correct and with their assistance he had been able to remove the 'cloud' that had been hanging over the works. He made special mention of the work of the Mechanics Institute in enabling young men to learn and raise themselves in the world. He "had always been proud of a man who had raised himself in this manner because he must have considerable tact and perseverance". He urged such young men to make the most of their opportunities since, economically speaking, things were 'just at the balance' and they had already seen foreign locomotives imported.

A more personal reminiscence of William's period at Stratford is provided by an anonymous former employee at the works writing in the Locomotive Railway Carriage and Wagon Review in 1936. William was an imposing man physically, six feet tall, heavily built and bearded. For these and possibly other reasons the workforce regarded him with some awe. In addition he was, like the other Worsdells we have considered, a very conscientious and correct man who clearly expected the same qualities in his workforce. In the early days of his tenure at Stratford he 'developed the rather nasty habit' of going into the workshops after 5pm during the last half-hour of the day's work. On one particular occasion our informant and his colleagues who had been engaged in converting an old wheel lathe into a cylinder boring machine had already put away their tools when William appeared unexpectedly. In some panic the workmen picked up anything to hand, hammers, spanners etc and began 'metal-bashing' with a vengeance. William asked the works manager what the men were engaged upon and having been told of the conversion thought for a few moments and then called out "Stop the work" before making off. Just on going home time the foreman arrived and said that no more work was to be done on this particular conversion as having seen the men at work William considered the result could never be a good one!

William's five years with the North Eastern Railway at Gateshead, until the succession of his younger brother Wilson in 1890, were a period of immense creativity. His initial task was to restore confidence and harmony after the acrimonious resignation of his predecessor, Alexander McDonnell, and yet in addition he designed some ten distinct locomotive types in that short period of office.

McDonnell had come to Gateshead in 1882 from the Inchicore works of the Great Southern and Western Railway of Ireland. He had enjoyed considerable success there rationalising the manufacture and maintenance of locomotives and in employing him at Gateshead the North Eastern Directors envisaged he would perform a similar task there after the benign and relaxed supervision of his predecessor of almost thirty years standing, Edward Fletcher.

On taking office McDonnell was horrified by the diversity of locomotive types running on the line, the complete lack of any standardisation of components and the consequent high engineering costs. Almost his first act was to initiate a survey of the company's workshop facilities. He found a very bad state of affairs with out of date equipment and poor working practices. The company grasped the opportunity to implement McDonnell's recommendations on workshop reorganisation with the result that by 1884 a substantial programme of investment at Gateshead, Darlington and York had been completed. In this sense McDonnell's legacy to the company was the valuable one of workshops equipped to the latest practice which placed the company well in terms of engineering efficiency.

But unfortunately this was not to be the whole story for McDonnell. In his zeal to reorganise and rationalise he exhibited a wonderful ability to antagonize the more entrenched members of the company's staff used to the comfortable existence of the Fletcher era. To them it must have seemed that McDonnell wanted change for the sake of change. He particularly incensed footplate staffs, designing a locomotive to be driven from the left hand side of the footplate rather than the right. The new arrangement,very sensibly, enabled the driver to keep a better look out for the signals but did not please the very conservative North Eastern drivers.

This was but one example of the obstructiveness encountered by McDonnell and apparently lacking the will or ability to cajole he resigned from the company in 1884 in some bitterness, after less than two years service. Following his departure there was an interregnum of several months during which time the General Manager of the Company, Henry Tennant, assumed overall control of locomotive matters. It is interesting to note, however, that as is often the case in such unpromising circumstances, something good did emerge from this period, namely the fine express passenger 2-4-0 locomotives which have always been known at the "Tennants". Notwithstanding this, the Gateshead locomotive department must have been in some disarray when William took up the reins on 1st September 1885, joining his younger brother Wilson who was already with the company. William had been appointed at a Directors' meeting on 17th April at a salary of £3,000 per annum, a very large sum and as we have seen, twice that on offer at Stratford. He was a man of great experience, at Crewe, in America and at Stratford, still in his prime at the age of 47, and of commanding appearance and physique. Just the man to restore order and discipline on the North Eastern. In the event it seems that his assumption of office passed very smoothly—perhaps everyone was simply relieved that the McDonnell era was over—and William very soon had new designs of engine coming off the drawing board.

Appendix 1 provides a brief summary of William's design output in his five years at Gateshead.

Perhaps as a symbol of the new order he decided to introduce a serial designation of locomotive types hitting on the simple idea of using letters of the alphabet to denote each type. Class 'A', tank engines of the 2-4-2 wheel arrangement, thus emerged first early in 1886. These locomotives were very similar in layout and appearance to the 'M15' engines he had designed for the Great Eastern and it has been suggested that drawings sent from Stratford may have helped in the rapid production of the class. Used on short distance and branch line passenger trains a total of 60 engines of

T. W. Worsdell's first design for the North Eastern Railway, the 'A' class tank engines. These locomotives were remarkably similar to his 'M15' design for the Great Eastern Railway. *(K. Taylor collection)*

This 'B' class six-coupled tank engine was photographed at Annfield Plain in 1902. Number 74 was one of the eleven original non-compounded 'B1' engines.

(K. Taylor collection)

the type were built over the years at Gateshead works. With a non-driving axle at each end they became known as 'double enders' and after the 1923 grouping, in LNER days, were redesignated the 'F8' class. Almost inevitably the Joy valve gear was provided.

William's next design, the class 'B' tank engines of the 0-6-2 wheel arrangement,were the first six coupled compound goods locomotives to work in this country. They employed the Joy valve gear, and were to be the first of many two cylinder Worsdell-von Borries compound designs for his new employers. It has been observed that their use on freight traffic would have provided a very severe test of the compounding principle which worked best at high speeds and did not take kindly to low speed work with frequent stopping and starting. Perhaps a severe test was what William sought, and it is of interest to note that, as if to act as a control for the compounding experiment, ten very similar engines but with two high pressure cylinders only were built at the same time for comparative purposes. The latter were designated class 'B1'. Fifty of the compound engines were built, the first ten at Gateshead and the rest at Darlington from 1888. Ten 'B1s' were built at Darlington in 1886 and another solitary engine in 1888. Wilson Worsdell succeeded his elder brother as Locomotive Superintendent in 1890 and did not share William's enthusiasm for compounding or the Joy valve gear. After William had severed all connection with the North Eastern in 1893 Wilson set about systematically rebuilding William's compounds as simple locomotives and substituting Stephenson valve gear for that of Joy. The class 'B' engines were no exception and after some years service were rebuilt effectively becoming 'B1s'. In their new form they were to give many years of excellent service, becoming the 'N8' class on the LNER, and a number survived beyond nationalisation in 1948, not being scrapped by British Railways until the mid 1950's.

William's third design at Gateshead was an 0-6-0 goods engine, the class 'C'. These were needed to cope with the expanding volume of goods and mineral traffic on the line at that time. As before with class 'B', the locomotives were two cylinder compounds. One hundred and seventy-one of them were built in all over a period of eight years and again following the precedent established with class 'B' a smaller number of very similar engines, thirty in all, designated 'C1', were constructed as 'simples' with two high pressure cylinders. Again the compound locomotives were later rebuilt by Wilson Worsdell as simple engines and with the Joy valve gear replaced by the Stephenson type. In this form the 'C1' class, known as 'J21s' on the LNER, gave yeoman service. Many survived beyond

Number 963, built at Gateshead in 1889. An example of the 'C' class goods engine, a very numerous type mostly built as compounds and illustrating the commodious cabs provided by the humanitarian T. W. Worsdell.

(K. Taylor collection)

nationalisation, about twenty-five being active as late as 1953. Fortunately one example, NER No. 876 built at Gateshead in 1889 and latterly British Railways No 65033, has survived and can be seen splendidly restored in preservation at the North of England Open Air Museum at Beamish Hall, County Durham.

The class 'D' engines introduced in 1886 were of yet another wheel arrangement being 2-4-0 locomotives with 6ft. 8ins. diameter driving wheels and designed for express passenger work. The Worsdell-von Borries compound system was again used as was the Joy valve gear. Very handsome engines, the 'Ds' exhibited many of the characteristics of the express passenger engines William had designed at Stratford, most notably the continuous splasher over the driving wheels. Despite the fact that the prototype No. 1324 appeared at the Newcastle Exhibition of 1887, where it was much admired, only two of the type were actually built, even though in service the engines were said to burn 15% less fuel than non-compound types. The problem was said to be that the additional weight of the larger, low pressure cylinder was too much for the leading axle to bear

An official NER photograph of a 'D' class engine in original condition. Only two of this type were built. *(By courtesy of the National Railway Museum, York)*

and this led to unsteadiness when at speed. This was remedied by substituting a four wheel bogie for the leading axle thus rendering the two engines virtually identical to the class 'F' engines introduced in 1887. The second class 'D' engine No. 340 though not accorded the honour of display at an exhibition was also of interest in that as an experiment it was fitted when new in 1888 with 'Smiths Patent Piston Valves' developed by Walter Mackersie Smith, the Chief Draughtsman, for many years an influential voice in design matters at Gateshead and later in 1902 to play an important role in the introduction of the famous three cylinder compounds on the Midland Railway.

William's next design was an 0-6-0 tank engine the class 'E'. These were 'maid of all work' shunting and light goods locomotives. One hundred and twenty were built between 1886 and 1895, more than any other class of tank engine of this wheel arrangement on the NER. As shunting engines they were, of course, simple rather than compound locomotives and most, if not all, survived into LNER days as class 'J71'. Well over half came into British Railways ownership in 1948, an outstanding record of longevity.

A very attractive 'period' shot of an 'E' class tank engine complete with 'gaffers' with shunting poles.
(K. Taylor collection)

One member of the class, LNER No. 8286 built at Darlington in 1892, was painted in NER apple green livery, instead of the usual black of shunting engines, in May 1947 for special duties as the shunter at York station. The effect was so pleasing that the engine was repainted green again in 1950 after nationalisation, this time in the new British Railways passenger livery.

The class 'F' engines were, as mentioned previously, compound 4-4-0 express passenger locomotives that may be considered a development of the earlier class 'D'. 25 were constructed between 1887 and 1891. Again a 'simple' version, class 'F1', was brought out alongside the first ten of the compounds, also numbering ten engines. It seems clear that William considered the compounds superior in this case as all construction of the 4-4-0s after 1887 concentrated on the compound variant.

The class 'F' engines are of historical interest for the part they played in the 1888 'Race to Edinburgh'. This came about as a result of the rivalry between the two groups operating Anglo-Scottish services, the London &

North Western/Caledonian Railway (the West Coast route) and the Great Northern/North Eastern/North British Railways (the East coast route). The two routes were in fierce competition and constantly seeking to improve on the times of the other for the journey between the cities of London and Edinburgh. Each route sought to outdo the other on a day to day basis in the matter of 'ahead of schedule' arrival to such an extent that a 'racing' atmosphere developed. This reached a peak in the August of 1888 when

'F' class No. 117 in original compound form. This engine played a notable role in the 1888 'Race to Edinburgh'. *(K. Taylor collection)*

some very fast journeys were recorded on the East Coast route between York and Edinburgh by NER locomotives hauling the 'Flying Scotsman'. The fastest run of all it was claimed officially was that of 'F' class engine No. 117 which covered the 124½ miles from Newcastle to Edinburgh in 126 minutes with a load of 100 tons arriving at the Scottish capital 34 minutes ahead of time. Sceptical commentators, however, have sought to detract from this achievement pointing out that the 2-4-0 engines produced during the Tennant interregnum would certainly have been preferred to the 'F' class on such a run and that it has been pretty well established that there were two locomotives at the head of the Edinburgh train on that occasion. It is suggested that a "Tennant" was the 'train engine' with the class 'F' in front of it with its leading bogie providing additional stability and track holding at high speed. Whatever the exact role played by No. 117 in these historic events, there seems little doubt that the class 'F' compounds as built, despite their good looks and turn of speed, represented little, if any, improvement on the performance of the widely admired "Tennant" engines.

As with many other of William's compound designs, the locomotives were rebuilt as simple engines with piston valves and Stephenson valve gear by his younger brother, Wilson. They were redesignated as the 'D22' class by the LNER but did not survive until nationalisation.

The class 'F' engines although perhaps something of a disappointment in service were undeniably handsome and as built incorporated all of the features characteristic of William Worsdell's engines at both Stratford and Gateshead: the application of compounding on the Worsdell-von Borries system, the elegant continuous splasher over the driving wheels of four coupled passenger engines, the Joy valve gear and the Ramsbottom-type safety valves covered by a brass casing. Significantly too, William continued at Gateshead to show concern for locomotive crew comfort and, impressed by American practise during his stay there, further evolved the design of locomotive cab which he had begun to improve at Stratford. All of his tender engines were provided with a very comfortable, spacious and elegant cab fitted with twin side windows. In an earlier era enginemen had complained bitterly against the provision of all over cabs but the Worsdell cabs were seemingly welcomed and must have proved a boon on wet, windswept days in the often inhospitable north eastern terrain. Not that any locomotive cab could ever be perfect. The one that protected from the worst that winter offered could be unbearably hot in summer and it was also said of William's cabs that on some engine types the position of the side windows in relation to the natural driving position caused much inconvenience to the driver. These reservations aside the North Eastern was years ahead of other lines in this aspect of staff welfare, undoubtedly evidence of the kindly Quaker paternalism that William exhibited throughout his life and that was so typical of the 19th century Worsdells.

Not that William confined himself to engineering and welfare matters. Aesthetic considerations were always in his mind as can be judged from the photographs of any of his locomotives, and most revealingly from his habit of going to considerable lengths to hide from public view

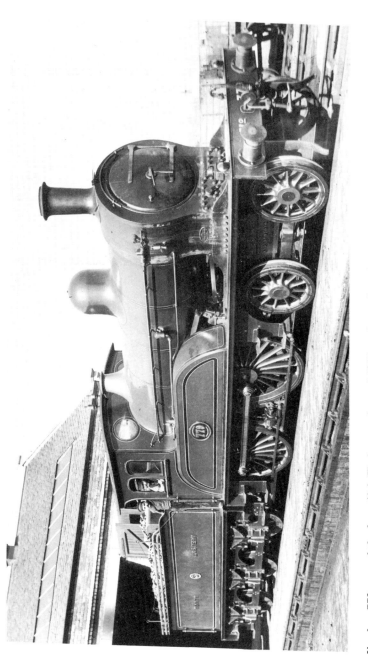

Number 779, one of the beautiful 'F' class engines of 1887, makes a fine sight at Haymarket shed, Edinburgh c.1900. The locomotive is in its original compound form.
(G. Tod collection/NRM, York)

unattractive parts of his engines such as the Westinghouse pump. Even the painting and decoration of his engines was important to him. We have already heard of his reintroduction of the royal blue livery on the Great Eastern. At Gateshead the practice had been to finish passenger locomotives in dark green. William embellished this considerably adding a wide crimson border and elaborate lining but after some years this was replaced with a more austere scheme by a Wilson Worsdell anxious to economise.

William's class 'G' locomotives were 2-4-0s of which twenty were built in 1887-88. Considered to be express passenger engines and with 6ft. diameter driving wheels they were nevertheless not intended for the most demanding work, but rather for secondary duties being based mainly in the Leeds and Hull areas and working to such places as Scarborough. Unusually for express passengers engines designed under William's auspices they were simple rather than compound engines although the Joy valve gear was employed. They were, it seems, unexceptional

'G' class No. 274 as originally built with the 2-4-0 wheel arrangement. These engines known as 'Waterburys' were the only T. W. Worsdell express type not built in the compound form. *(K. Taylor collection)*

engines but they earned themselves the nickname 'Waterburys' after the American make of watch, apparently because of their ability to keep to time on passenger trains. Between 1901-03 Wilson Worsdell predictably rebuilt them with the Stephenson valve gear and there is some evidence from the writings of such as the late Cecil J. Allen that their performance was thereby somewhat improved. The 'Waterburys', however, were not long lived and had been scrapped before the formation of the LNER at the grouping of 1923.

The 'G' class as rebuilt to a 4-4-0 is represented by No. 223.　　*(K. Taylor collection)*

The class 'H' engines introduced in 1888 were very small four wheeled tank locomotives for shunting at docks and on lightly laid sidings. Unusually for this type of duty inside cylinders were fitted. Class 'H' engines were so small that they could fit on to an engine turntable with much larger engines thus making them useful as shunting engines at railway workshops and engine sheds. Seventeen examples of the type were built between 1888-97 and somewhat surprisingly another five were constructed by the LNER as late as 1923, a tribute to the usefulness of this albeit very humble type. Many were sold by the NER to private concerns as colliery and factory shunters in the 1930s but at least one LNER No. 985 survived to see service on British Railways into the 1950s having become LNER class 'Y7'. This engine, one of the 1923 batch built at Darlington, was sold to the National Coal Board in December 1952 and used at Bentinck Colliery in Nottingham for a number of years. It is now working in preservation at the Great Central Railway at Loughborough, Leicestershire. One of the original Gateshead engines NER No. 1310, sold for colliery use in the 1930s, worked until 1965 at various sites in County Durham until acquired for preservation and subsequent use on the Middleton Railway at Leeds.

The small 'H' class engines were designed for shunting on dock lines and in railway depots. This official view illustrates the simplicity of the design. Happily two of the 22 built have survived into preservation. *(K. Taylor collection)*

The class 'H' engines were unusual in having a boiler without a steam dome. This was not a whim on William's part, but was due to the fact that class 'H' boilers were interchangeable with those on the 'H1' class, two small six coupled engines for workshop shunting which sported a crane, the swinging jib of which would have fouled a steam dome.

Number 590, an 'H1' crane engine, designed for work around railway workshops. One of only two built. *(By courtesy of the National Railway Museum, York)*

In his next design William seems to have turned the clock back to 1870 and beyond, for after producing three express passenger designs at Gateshead with four coupled driving wheels he resorted to single driving wheel locomotives in his classes 'I' and 'J'. This was a radical departure from previous NER practise but the higher axle loads allowable on modern heavier track made the idea of a single wheeler feasible, and it was felt that there was enough work on fast trains over relatively flat terrain to justify the change. Worsdell-von Borries compounding was employed and the Joy valve gear. In order to support the extra weight of the compounded cylinders a leading bogie was employed giving a 4-2-2 wheel arrangement. The first class 'I' locomotive was turned out in 1888 with a high pressure cylinder of 18ins. diameter and 24ins. stroke and a low pressure cylinder of 26ins. by 24ins. Soon after its appearance it was felt that a more powerful engine of the same type should be provided. Thus was born class 'J' with a larger firebox and cylinders increased in size to 20ins. by 24ins. and 28ins. by 24ins. This increase in cylinder size posed all kinds of design problems since they were now too large to sit side by side between the frameplates of the engine. Very substantial redesign of the cylinder layout, the position of the steam chests and the valve gear was necessary. It seems that an opportunity was missed here in that with the steam chests on the outside of the frames an external link valve gear driven from an extension of the driving axle would have proved ideal. For whatever reason this obvious solution was rejected in favour of a more complex, but hidden, modification of the Joy system. The latter proved to be a very bad layout leading to many breakdowns in service.

The 'I' and 'J' class engines were a throwback, 'single wheelers' built well after the adoption of the 4-4-0 arrangement for express passenger work. They were ideal, however, for the fast running with light trains which characterised the 'racing' period of the 1880s and 90s. 'I' class No. 1530 is shown here at Scarborough in its original form as a compound. *(K. Taylor collection)*

Number 1517, of the larger 'J' class single wheelers, shown in original form as a compound with outside steam chests.

(By courtesy of the National Railway Museum, York)

Though similar in general appearance the class 'J' engines, with their external steam chests and repositioned sandboxes, were immediately distinguishable from the slightly smaller class 'I'. The former boasted driving wheels of no less than 7ft. 7ins. diameter against the 7ft. of class 'I'. Ten class 'I' engines were built between 1888-90, and the same number of class 'J' in 1889-90.

These single wheelers put up some very creditable performances, the larger engines in particular tackling heavy main line trains between Newcastle and Edinburgh. On one notable occasion a speed of 86 mph on the level was recorded by class 'J' No. 1518 hauling a train of 223 tons, an outstanding achievement implying an output of 1,068 Horse Power. Notwithstanding such heroics the unsatisfactory layout of steam chests and valve gear led to the early rebuilding of the class 'J' engines in 1894/95 by Wilson Worsdell as simple engines with Smith's Patent Piston Valves.

The 'J' class, rebuilt as simple engines and with the steam chests repositioned, were very handsome. Here No. 1519 is shown leaving York. *(K. Taylor collection)*

In this modified form the engines continued to astonish, No.1517 setting a record on 12th December 1904 by covering the 80¾ miles between York and Newcastle at an average speed of 61.5 mph. At around the same time they also worked the non stop Leeds-Scarborough expresses running to a 75 minute schedule for the 67½ miles.

The smaller class 'I' engines, not suffering from the design problems of their sisters, survived longer as compounds not being rebuilt until 1900-02. The class 'I', and as rebuilt, the class 'J' engines were undeniably handsome as well as fast and constitute a fascinating diversion in Gateshead practice under William Worsdell.

William's final design for the NER before retirement was very much of an anti-climax and in complete contrast to the elegant single wheelers. The class 'K' engines were in fact the tiniest locomotives designed under William's aegis, being little four coupled dock shunters weighing only 15½ tons. Five were built to work on the dock lines at Hull in 1890. They were classified 'Y8' by the LNER and, as is often the case with very humble

Only five of the tiny 'K' class engines were built, for dock shunting. This delightful view at Newcastle Quayside shows No. 563 with fine supporting cast.

(K. Taylor collection)

machines, gave many years of service the last survivor still being active in British Railways' ownership in the early 1950s.

In addition to supervising the construction of new locomotives to his own designs William had, of course, responsibility for the existing fleet of locomotives. It is perhaps interesting to record his part in rebuilding two of the locomotive types of one of his predecessors Edward Fletcher. The first was the latter's '901' class, express passenger 2-4-0s built between 1872 and 1882 and which had already been subject to one rebuilding by McDonnell involving the contentious move to left hand driving. William embarked on a further rebuilding and the result was very pleasing to look at. One example of this class, No. 910, forms part of the collection at the National Railway Museum at York. Also part of the York collection is the very attractive tank engine 'Aerolite', No. 66. Originally designed as a 2-2-2 well-tank locomotive by Fletcher it was according to official records rebuilt by William in 1886 with auxiliary side tanks. In fact it was probably almost an entirely new engine. At a later date, said to have been 1892 and under Wilson Worsdell's auspices, but probably earlier under William's direction, 'Aerolite' was rebuilt again as a two cylinder compound with 13½ins. and 18ins. diameter cylinders. In order to accommodate the larger cylinders the leading axle was replaced by a bogie giving a 4-2-2 wheel arrangement. Finally in 1902 Wilson Worsdell rebuilt 'Aerolite' yet again and this time, although remaining a compound, it emerged as a 2-2-4, a very unusual wheel arrangement but not a unique one on the NER. The engine spent many years pulling the Chief Engineer's private coach on tours of inspection over the system and was placed in the original York Railway Museum in 1934. It is thus the only Worsdell-von Borries compound locomotive on the North Eastern to have survived in that form.

In all during his period of office at Gateshead William was responsible for the design and construction of 544 locomotives, no less than 269 of which employed the Worsdell-von Borries compounding system.

William had always suffered badly from asthma and it is thought that it was this that caused him to offer his resignation on health grounds.

Mr John Dent Dent, the Chairman of the company, wrote to William from his private address, Ribston Hall, Wetherby, on 9th August 1890 informing him of the great regret of all the Board members on receiving his letter of resignation and wondering if he might reconsider his position, if arrangements could be made to lighten his workload. Mr Dent assured William that his proposed resignation was "very painful to me — I have felt so secure since I have got to know you, as to the conduct and management of your great department, that much of my anxiety and responsibility as

Chairman seemed to be removed—I am selfish enough to rather dread making a fresh start and having to feel my way with new people. I can only say that when the time comes to part I shall be very much grieved....."

Despite this appeal William did not feel able to withdraw his resignation which was accepted on 19th September 1890 by the Board to take effect from the end of the month. On 1st October he was succeeded as Locomotive Superintendent and Chief Mechanical Engineer by his brother Wilson who had been Assistant Mechanical Engineer at Gateshead initially under McDonnell and then under his elder brother.

The present author has been unable to discover reports of any presentation in respect of William's resignation in 1890. Quite possibly no such event took place then as a result of William's poor health and probable absence. (Certainly there is evidence that Wilson Worsdell was exercising de facto control at Gateshead before October of that year.)

After his premature retirement at the age of 52, William was retained by the NER as Consulting Engineer until 1893 when he formally severed connections with the company. His role as consultant was seemingly a nominal one,although his retainer for 1891-92 was set at £1,000 per annum.

It was during the period of his consultancy that William, by now restored to better health, was the subject of a commemorative presentation at Gateshead. A committee headed by Mr R. Stirling (the Works Manager), Mr Vincent Raven (the Deputy Locomotive Superintendent) and Mr J. E. Gray was set up to realise the wishes of 'the large mass of employees' for some lasting recognition of his work. A musical evening was thus held at the North Eastern Railway Literary Institute on 31st May 1892 at which William was presented with his portrait in oils by Mr J. H. Campbell and an illuminated address. (John Hodgson Campbell (1855-1927) was a noted local portraitist and landscape artist living in Pilgrim Street, Newcastle. Trained at Edinburgh he exhibited at the Royal Academy between 1884 and 1894 and also at the New Water Colour Society in London. He was a founder member of both the Bewick Club and the Pen and Palette Club in Newcastle).

A large number attended the function including Wilson Worsdell. The presentation was made by Mr George Kendall of Heaton Junction, one of the longest serving officers of the locomotive department. The address embellished with photographs of the workshops was produced by a Mr Gordon of the Felling firm of Messrs. W.Scott and Company. The inscription was as follows: "To T. W. Worsdell, Esq.—On the occasion of placing your portrait in the Lecture Hall of the North Eastern Railway

The illuminated address presented to T. W. Worsdell on his final retirement from Gateshead in 1892 by the members of the North Eastern Railway Literary Institute.

Literary Institution, Gateshead, we, the members, take this opportunity of expressing our gratitude for the very valuable services you rendered towards obtaining it; and the subscribers generally who are connected with the Northern Division of the Locomotive, Carriage and Waggon Departments of this railway desire also to convey to you their sense of the many kindnesses shown during the time you were actively engaged amongst them. We trust in the repose which you have sought you may live in the enjoyment of health, and have every happiness".

In his remarks Mr Kendall alluded to the regret that was felt when William had had to retire and said he was sure that "all would be heartily pleased to see him once again amongst them and looking so much improved". The large and enthusiastic audience would show him that Gateshead could not forget its friends. A letter was read out from Mr George Graham, the Assistant Locomotive Superintendent of the Northern division at Darlington apologising for his inability to attend and praising William in eulogistic terms. Fortunately this letter has survived amongst the Worsdell family papers. In it Mr Graham says of William "he has been to me, both publicly and in private, a kind and considerate friend" and later "although he maintained strict discipline amongst all classes of employees, his impartial dealing was always attended with kindness".

Mr Kendall also praised William's approachability and his desire to assist the staff in any way possible notably in the establishment of the 'splendid' Institute "which provided every opportunity for scientific study and self improvement".

William responded with typical modesty thanking those present for the warmth of the welcome but insisting that while at Gateshead he had merely "done his duty and nothing more". He felt that the staff had gone to a great deal of expense and effort to perpetuate his memory and drew applause with the suggestion that his portrait be allowed to be hung at the Institute. William suggested that much of the credit for the provision of the Institute lay not with himself, but with his late friend Mr T. E. Harrison, the former Chief Engineer of the Company. He also asked that the same consideration be shown to his successor (his brother, Wilson) as had been shown to him during his period of office.

Commenting on the presentation a diarist in the *Newcastle Chronicle* of 1st June 1892 recalled an occasion when trouble "in the shape of labour difficulties" threatened. William's patient hearing of all the grievances and the tact he displayed in removing them formed "an instance of good leadership that should not be forgotten".

Throughout his period at Gateshead Works William had in fact not lived

William Worsdell in old age.

in the town, but on the other side of the Tyne at 'Blythswood' on the Osborne Road in the select Newcastle suburb of Jesmond. Nevertheless there is no doubt that the Locomotive Superintendent at Gateshead would have been a considerable force in the life of that town. There had been locomotive workshops there since the Newcastle and Darlington Railway had established a small facility in 1844. This was transferred to a new 30 acre site in 1852-54, and when the North Eastern Railway was formed in 1854 Gateshead became the headquarters for locomotive building and maintenance. By the end of the 19th century the company was easily the most important employer of labour in the town, but the directors were concerned about the high level of wages that could be commanded by the workmen as a result of competition from engineering companies and shipbuilders on the Tyne. This, together with the lack of room for expansion on the constricted site, were the main reasons which led the company to concentrate locomotive work at the Darlington factory which had been improved and extended in the period 1897-1910. The Chief

A view of the erecting shop at the NER Gateshead Works. Shortage of space and skilled labour resulted in new locomotive construction being transferred to Darlington in 1910. *(By courtesy of the National Railway Museum, York)*

Mechanical Engineer and his staff moved to Darlington on 1st October 1910 and in that same year the last new locomotive was built at Gateshead which subsequently endured a much diminished status as a repair shop.

From 1886-92 William served as a member of the Council of the Institution of Mechanical Engineers. He had originally joined the Institution in 1864 and retained his membership, apart from the period of his sojourn in America and for a while afterwards, until 1915 shortly before his death. He became a member of the Institution of Civil Engineers in 1884. In retirement at Arnside he continued to take an interest in engineering matters. He undertook occasional consulting work and still retained his enthusiasm for the compounded steam locomotive. Three further patents in this connection were granted to William in association with August von Borries and Richard Lapage. Patent No. 7647 of 1892 specified "the use in a compound locomotive engine of an improved construction and arrangement of valves and valve cases whereby the engine can at will be used either as a compound engine or as an ordinary high pressure engine..." The ability, at will and in the simplest manner

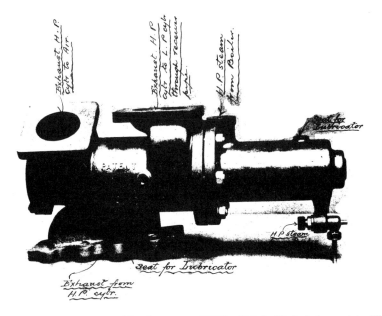

The 'change valve' covered by the patent of 1892 which facilitated change 'at will' from compound to simple high pressure operation.

possible to convert a compound locomotive, fuel efficient when running at speed, to a simple high pressure engine when ascending an incline or starting a heavy train or when shunting was clearly vital to the success of the principle. Compound locomotive design was further refined under Patent No. 6487 of 1900. This specification described an automatic apparatus for changing from two cylinder simple operation at low speeds to compound operation at high speeds and vice versa. This was facilitated by the employment of an exhaust valve of small surface area at the outlet of the HP cylinder combined with one of the known starting valves. The new valve allowed exhaust steam from the HP cylinder to escape to the chimney at low engine speed, but held the exhaust steam in check in the receiver and at high speed the rapidly succeeding 'puffs' opened the starting valve under pressure and closed the special exhaust valve, the working then becoming compound.

The three engineers' final patent collaboration was No. 22906 of 1900 which described yet further improvements in valves for use in compound engines.

With hindsight the development of the Worsdell-von Borries compound engines on the NER must be judged as something of a cul-de-sac. Although Wilson Worsdell was second in command to his brother and must have at least acquiesced in William's protracted love affair with compounding, he lost no time after assuming control himself in rebuilding the vast majority of his brother's compound locomotives as simple engines. (The Joy valve gear also received short shrift). Nevertheless, railways in Britain and overseas had compound locomotives built on the Worsdell-von Borries system. The type found favour on overseas lines such as the Bengal-Nagpur and Indian Midland Railways and it has been estimated that at least 1,000 were in service by the early 1890s. They never enjoyed wide popularity on other British lines although William Adams, William's sometime predecessor at Stratford, experimented rather unsuccessfully with the type on the London and South Western Railway in 1888. More notably the Belfast and Northern Counties Railway and its successor the Northern Counties Committee built seven 4-4-0 express passenger engines on the principle between 1901 and 1907 which were very successful.

A Wolseley 8HP car of the type in which William Worsdell crossed Wrynose Pass in 1907.

8 h.p.
A WONDERFUL HILL-CLIMBER.

William's engineering interests always extended beyond railways notably embracing the application of steam to other forms of traction. A surviving notebook of his started in the 1860's, the period when he was employed at his uncle Thomas' works in Birmingham, reveals a particular interest in steam road vehicles and in marine engines. Notes on no less than 20 steam cars and carriages are to be found in these pages. And his interest was not just academic. In about 1875 he had a steam tricycle built at Crewe Locomotive Works. Later in retirement he owned a Stanley steam car and a steam launch. The steam car was disposed of about 1904 and a 12 HP Wolseley motor car obtained. Yet another notebook records outings and mileages in these and subsequent vehicles. The first mention of the Wolseley is on 15th November 1904 but by August 1905 a new 8 HP Wolseley had been obtained as a replacement for the first. Contemporary advertisements promoted this model as 'a wonderful hill-climber' and William was to put this claim to the test in spectacular fashion. The *Westmorland Gazette* of 7th September 1907 informs us that 'on Wednesday last week an 8 HP Wolseley motor car belonging to Mr T. W. Worsdell, of Arnside, succeeded in crossing Wrynose Pass from Little Langdale into the Duddon Valley' and that local people were certain that no car had previously negotiated the pass. William and his son Wilson

This very grand Wolseley followed the 8HP model in William's ownership.

Crosfield Worsdell together with their driver, Mr Green, took part in this heroic feat which was achieved with more than a little difficulty, the two Worsdells having to demount and walk over one particularly rough section. Interestingly a later Rolls Royce advertisement of circa 1910 claimed that one of their vehicles had recently been the first to cross Wrynose but there seems no doubt that the honour lies with William's humble Wolseley.

In May 1909 the notebook records the arrival of a very superior new machine an 18 HP Wolseley Siddeley Laundalette (Maker's serial number 4198) His last new car was a 14 HP Alldays and Onions in January 1912. William is said to have played a role in the design of this last manufacturer's cars but the present author has not been able to corroborate this.

William was a talented miniaturist in water colours and had an interest in botany. He was fascinated by boats of all kinds spending much time during holidays and later in retirement on the waters of Morecambe Bay. Rowing and sailing boats were favoured as well as the steam launch already referred to. Even a vessel powered by an oil engine was put through its paces. Two of these boats were called the 'Undine' and the 'Verena', this much is clear from a doggerel verse 'The Stonycroft Alphabet' which survives in his notebook.

William took the opportunity afforded by early retirement to travel. He and Mary journeyed to the Holy Land in January and February of 1900, travelling by train across France to Marseilles and thence by the steam yacht 'Argonaut'. They called at Syracuse, Piraeus, Constantinople, Jaffa (for Jerusalem and Bethlehem), Alexandria (for Cairo and the pyramids), Malta and Naples (for Pompeii) before returning to Marseilles.

In September of the following year, 1901, William and Mary revisited the United States of America after a gap of thirty years. They travelled out from Liverpool to New York on the S.S. 'Canadian' of the Leyland Line taking 11½ days for the crossing and spent three hectic weeks visiting friends and places of interest in the eastern USA. On their day of arrival they quite fortuitously met members of the Pennsylvania Railroad's Roberts family, appropriately at New York's Pennsylvania Station, and later stayed with them at Westchester outside Philadelphia. The couple made a sentimental journey to Altoona staying at the Logan House Hotel. They had no difficulty locating the streets where they and their friends had lived but marvelled at the large stores and electric trams which had so changed the town. On the following morning G. W. Strattan, an old colleague of William's called and took him to the Pennsylvania Railroad's workshops. William's diary gratifyingly records that 'the foreman and others were very enthusiastic in their welcome to me as I passed through. I could hardly get from one place to another and some others called on me at the hotel'.

Thereafter William and Mary travelled to Washington where William was much impressed by the grandeur of the buildings and by the Library of Congress. George Washington's house at Mount Vernon was visited as was the National Museum where William noted the two historic British built locomotives, the 'Stourbridge Lion' of 1829 and the 'John Bull' of 1831 from the Camden and Amboy Railroad. The couple ended their visit in the Boston area. At Haverhill they were shown through the birthplace of John Greenleaf Whittier (1807-92), the Quaker poet and politician, who had been a prominent opponent of slavery. They also visited his house at nearby Amesbury by this time already maintained as a museum to his memory. Whittier, had in 1886 contributed a preface to the 'Gospel of Divine Help' by Edward Worsdell, William's cousin. The last days of the visit were spent around Harvard and Cambridge visiting the houses of Nathaniel Hawthorne, Ralph Waldo Emerson and H. D. Thoreau and their graves at Sleepy Hollow, Concord. Whilst in Boston William's eye was caught by the latest steam car advertised as being of 'a thousand pounds weight and a thousand dollars price'.

The couple returned safely to Britain from Boston on the S.S. 'Cestrian' despite having had their trunk of warm clothing for the voyage 'mislaid' by the American Express Company! Typically William spent much of the crossing worrying about the welfare of the cattle who formed the main cargo of the 'Cestrian'.

Ever the innovator William had 'Stonycroft' equipped with acetylene gas lighting in March 1907. His notebook contains a photograph of generating equipment (supplied and installed by Messrs L. Airey & Co of Kendal) as well as details of the capital and running costs. At this time electricity was beginning to be adopted for household use but the vast majority of urban homes, if they had any 'mains' lighting at all, would have been 'town gas' lit. In rural areas neither option was available. William opted for acetylene whilst a few years earlier another famous north eastern engineer, the first Lord Armstrong, lit his remote country house at Cragside, Northumberland with electricity generated by water power, the first such application in the world.

Yet another of his interests was the dialect speech of the Yorkshire Dales and the area around his adoptive home in what we now call Cumbria. And his notebook also reveals the meaning of the private sign language used by tramps.

William Worsdell died at 'Stonycroft' on 28th June 1916 at the age of 78, one day before his fifty-first wedding anniversary. His wife Mary, six years his junior, and who had born him six children, three in America, survived him by two years. He left estate valued at £67,346 and was buried at the Friends' Meeting House, Yealand Conyers, where he and Mary had married.

The *Crewe Guardian* reporting in 1905 the death of Mr Lawrence Ramage, a former colleague at Crewe, said of William, then long removed from the town, "a more kindly hearted man never breathed".

'Stonycroft' at Arnside built by William Worsdell from 1879 as a holiday home. He died there in 1916.

The Locomotive Engineers

WORSDELL, VON BORRIES & LAPAGES SYSTEM PATENT COMPOUND ENGINE.

Sole Representatives,
TAITE & CARLTON,
63, QUEEN VICTORIA STREET.
LONDON, E.C.

Metropolitan Buildings,
63, Queen Victoria Street,
London, July 4th *189*3
E.C.

Patented in

THE UNITED KINGDOM
THE UNITED STATES OF AMERICA
FRANCE
GERMANY
RUSSIA
BELGIUM
AUSTRIA
SPAIN
ITALY
INDIA
CANADA
CAPE OF GOOD HOPE
SOUTH AUSTRALIA
NEW ZEALAND
VICTORIA
ARGENTINE REPUBLIC
BRAZIL
QUEENSLAND AND OTHER COUNTRIES

W. Worsdell Esq

North Eastern Railway

Gateshead.

Dear Sir,

Change Valve.

In reply to your favor of the 3rd inst, we beg to send you herewith drawing No 1001, showing the change valve fitted to the smoke box of one of your Compound Goods Engines.

In getting out the drawing for the valve we made several alter ations in detail for the valve shown on the enclosed drawing, but these alterations in no way affect the general arrangements of the valve. We have thought it best to alter the direction of the H.P. exhaust pipe, so as to give a more direct exhaust, and we have also put the flange for admitting H.P. steam on the top of piston case instead of at the side.

We enclose a photo-print of the change valve as made.

We shall be glad to receive particulars of the results of your trials in due course. Yours faithfully,

Taite & Carlton

An 1893 letter to Wilson Worsdell from Messrs Taite and Carlton, agents for the (T. W.) Worsdell-von Borries compounding system. Eighteen territories covered by the patent are listed.

110

VI

THE LOCOMOTIVE ENGINEERS

(ii) Wilson Worsdell

Wilson Worsdell, the tenth of Nathaniel and Mary Worsdell's children and their fourth son, was born on 7th September 1850 at Monks Coppenhall near Crewe, his father by this time having moved there in the railway service from Liverpool.

A cricketing group taken at Ackworth School, Yorkshire, probably in 1866. Wilson Worsdell standing fifth from left.

In the by then established Worsdell custom he was sent to the Friends' school at Ackworth in 1860 remaining there until the second half of 1866. A letter to his father from Ackworth dated 23rd May 1866 shows Wilson's beautiful 'copper plate' script at this time. On leaving school he returned to Crewe to a job in the drawing office of the London and North Western Railway. He stayed only six months however for in July 1867 he travelled in his brother William's footsteps to the Pennsylvania Railroad's Altoona workshops in the United States. Taken on as an engineering pupil Wilson at this time would have been ultimately responsible to Edward Williams, the superintendent of motive power and machinery, and who in 1870 was to become one of the principals of the famed Baldwin Locomotive Works of Philadelphia. As in the case of his brother, very little is known about Wilson's stay in America save that he looked back with pleasure on his time there. William returned to Crewe in August 1871 to take over as Works

An extract from a letter written to his father Nathaniel from Ackworth School in 1866 illustrates the very fine hand of the 15 year old Wilson Worsdell.

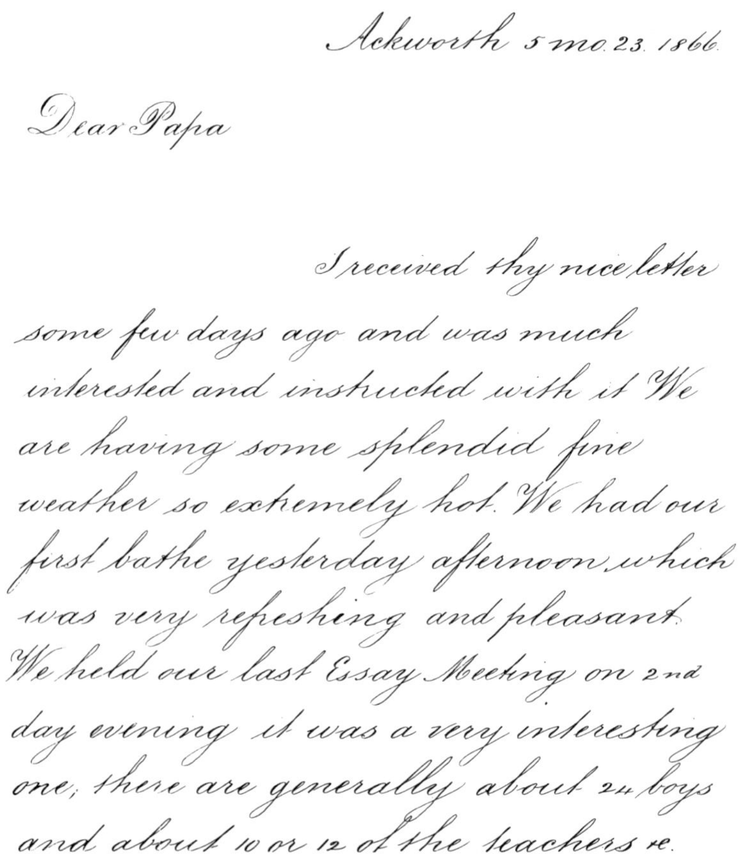

Ackworth 5 mo. 23. 1866.

Dear Papa

I received thy nice letter some few days ago and was much interested and instructed with it We are having some splendid fine weather so extremely hot. We had our first bathe yesterday afternoon, which was very refreshing and pleasant. We held our last Essay Meeting on 2nd day evening it was a very interesting one, there are generally about 24 boys and about 10 or 12 of the teachers &c.

Wilson Worsdell (second from right) photographed with fellow LNWR apprentices at Crewe c.1870.

Manager under Locomotive Superintendent Francis Webb and it seems very likely that Wilson accompanied him at that time.

Thus we see at a very early stage that Wilson's career curiously followed William's. It would not be unfair to suggest that this continued to be so until the time of William's final retirement from the North Eastern Railway in 1893 when Wilson was forty three years old.

On his return to England Wilson worked briefly in the locomotive erecting shop at Crewe Works before transferring to the drawing office during 1872. After two years Francis Webb sent him to Stafford to serve as assistant foreman at the locomotive sheds there. His qualities must have impressed for in 1876 he was promoted to be foreman at the much more important Bushbury engine sheds at Wolverhampton. Promotion came once more as he was given charge of the locomotive sheds at Chester in 1877. He spent more than five years here and during this time married. The ceremony took place on Thursday 1st June 1882 at St John's Church, Hanley, Staffordshire. His bride was Mary Elizabeth Bradford, then aged 25. She was the daughter of George and Mary Bradford of Hanley. Mr Bradford, formerly a Sea Captain, was a linen draper. The venue for the wedding presumably indicates that Mary was not disposed to join the Friends. Certainly Wilson held to his Quakerism transferring from the

The very fine diptych illuminated manuscript, illustrated on the two pages above, presented to Wilson Worsdell by the grateful locomotive men of

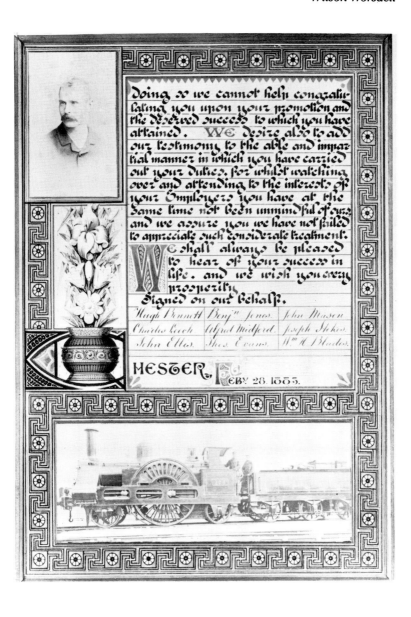

doing so we cannot help congratulating you upon your promotion and the deserved success to which you have attained. WE desire also to add our testimony to the able and impartial manner in which you have carried out your duties, for whilst watching over and attending to the interests of your Employers you have at the same time not been unmindful of ours and we assure you we have not failed to appreciate such considerate treatment. We shall always be pleased to hear of your success in life, and we wish you every prosperity.

Signed on our behalf.

Hugh Bennett	Benj.ⁿ Jones	John Mason
Charles Each	Alfred Midford	Joseph Stokes
John Ellos	Thos. Evans	Wᵐ H. Blades

CHESTER, FEBY. 28. 1855.

Chester on his departure for Gateshead in 1883. The locomotive *Cornwall* depicted is by happy coincidence preserved at Crewe.

Cheshire Monthly Meeting to the Hardshaw West Meeting in December 1878 and again to the Newcastle Meeting in October 1883 after his move to Gateshead to join the North Eastern Railway.

Wilson and Mary had set up home at 'The Laurels', Tarvin Road, Great Boughton, Chester and it was here on 16th February 1883, shortly before their move to the North East, that their only child, Geoffrey, was born. Unlike his father and the other male Worsdells brought up in the Quaker tradition, Geoffrey was to be educated, not at Ackworth, but at Charterhouse originally a monastic foundation.

Wilson's popularity with the men at Chester can be judged from the illuminated address presented to him at the time of his departure. The address, which survives in the ownership of Wilson's grandson, Brigadier Geoffrey Worsdell, is as follows:

"Sir,
Your connection with the London and North Western Railway Company being about to cease in consequence of your appointment to the office of Asst. Superintendent of the North Eastern Railway Company we, the drivers, firemen and shedmen in the services of the former company at the steam shed at Chester take the opportunity of expressing to you and recording our acknowledgement of the kindness and consideration you have at all times shown to us during the term of your management at Chester extending over a period of five years. We much regret your removal from amongst us but whilst doing so we cannot help congratulating you upon your promotion and the deserved success to which you have attained. We desire also to add our testimony to the able and impartial manner in which you have carried out your duties, for whilst watching over and attending to the interests of your employers you have at the same time not been unmindful of ours, and we assure you we have not failed to appreciate such considerate treatment. We shall always be pleased to hear of your success in life, and we wish you every prosperity.
Signed on our behalf
Hugh Bennett, Benjamin Jones, John Mason, Charles Leech, Alfred Midford, Joseph Stokes, John Ellis, Thos. Evans, Wm. H. Blades.
Chester, February 28th 1883"

Whilst Wilson was still at Chester William left the LNWR, taking up his post with the Great Eastern Railway at Stratford in 1881. Now surely Wilson would be able to develop his potential fully, no longer in his brother's imposing shadow. Fate was to decree otherwise as we have seen and

Wilson Worsdell (1850-1920) in maturity.

Wilson was required to be patient for many more years before he could finally throw off the mantle of 'little brother'. However, it must have been in great anticipation that he applied for, and obtained in March 1883, the position of Assistant Mechanical Engineer to the prosperous North Eastern Railway at Gateshead. This was under Alexander McDonnell the Company's 'new broom' from Ireland whose tenure of office, which had commenced in November 1882, was to be so short and explosive. As an early McDonnell appointee Wilson was probably initially tarred with the same brush as his chief by the conservative Geordies but they must have taken him to their hearts for he was to stay on after McDonnell's departure in 1884 and eventually completed 27 years service with the NER retiring at the end of May 1910.

On arrival at Gateshead Wilson's family occupied 'Greenesfield House', a large detached residence immediately adjacent to the locomotive works in Mulgrave Terrace. It was to be their home for the whole of their stay in the North East. In more recent times the building housed the local health authority's Greenesfield Dental Clinic but it has now been demolished.

Henry Tennant, the General Manager, took on overall responsibility for locomotives from the time of McDonnell's resignation until William

Worsdell's apppointment. The celebrated 'Tennant' 2-4-0s produced in this period in fact owed much to the ideas of the 34 years old Wilson Worsdell, the senior remaining locomotive engineer at Gateshead Works and chairman of the locomotive design committee. The result was an engine of sufficient power to handle the east coast expresses but which at the same time incorporated those design features, such as exhaust cocks and right handed drive, whose abandonment by McDonnell had led to much of the uproar. In short, as O. S. Nock has observed, the design was 'a model of tact, sound engineering and real aesthetic charm'. Twenty engines were built, ten each at Darlington and Gateshead and they were both extremely successful and popular with the men. The 'Tennants' immediately took over haulage of the heaviest expresses between York and Edinburgh and later played a central part in the famous 1888 'Race to Edinburgh' consistently covering the York to Newcastle section (80.6 miles) in 80-85 minutes in the August of that year. As we have seen in the previous chapter it seems likely that a 'Tennant' locomotive also played a role in the record breaking Newcastle to Edinburgh run at the same time.

Despite his association with the successful 'Tennants' However, promotion was not to come rapidly to Wilson. We can only guess at the

Wilson Worsdell, c.1890, at about the time of his appointment as Locomotive Superintendent of the North Eastern Railway.

onflicting emotions he must have felt when he heard that his elder brother was coming north to take over as Locomotive Superintendent. At the very least the two men had widely differing views on locomotive design, most notably on the issue of compounding. William clearly valued the abilities of the younger man though. Within a month of the former's arrival on 1st September 1885 Wilson was redesignated Assistant Locomotive Superintendent of the Northern Division and his salary increased from £500 to £600 per annum. Wilson was evidently prepared to bide his time at Gateshead and use the years of William's superintendency to gain experience and to develop his own engineering and design ideas. Of the two men William, 12 years the senior and physically the more imposing, was certainly the more commanding presence. Henry, William's son, who served an apprenticeship under the two brothers, recalled that his father's appearance in the works produced a 'red alert' whereas Wilson only evoked a 'yellow'.

William's retirement on health grounds from the end of September 1890 created an opening for Wilson much earlier than he could have anticipated and no-one was better placed than he to step into the Superintendent's post. Wilson took over from the 1st October at a salary of £1,100 per annum notably less than the £3,000 commanded by his brother five years earlier. His tenure was to be a long one of twenty years and one of continuous advance in traffic terms for the North Eastern requiring ever more powerful locomotives for passenger and freight working. He was fortunate that for most of those twenty years he was surrounded by outstanding colleagues. George Gibb was an exceptionally able General Manager from 1891-1906 and on the locomotive side Wilson's assistants were Vincent Litchfield Raven, Assistant Mechanical Engineer 1893-1910, and Walter Smith, the long serving Chief Draughtsman, until his death in 1906.

Appendix II gives a summary of Wilson's locomotive designs for the NER over his twenty years as Locomotive Superintendent and Chief Mechanical Engineer.

Wilson carried on the system of class designation originated by his brother. His first design was therefore the class 'L' somewhat prosaic six coupled tank engines for shunting. Of their kind they were rather large machines but only ten were ever constructed in 1891/92 at Gateshead. Nevertheless, some pointers to the future were apparent, for example Stephenson's link gear was used in preference to the Joy valve gear. The 'L' class engines were very long lived being redesignated as class 'J73' by the LNER. All survived nationalisation being withdrawn from service in the 1950s.

This 'L' class 'maid-of-all-work', No. 551, dated from 1891 and was photographe
at Tyne Dock. *(K. Taylor collectio*

The first major design to emerge under the new regime was the 'M1' clas
introduced in 1892. This represented a significant break with the desig
practices of the recent past. Wilson rejected the notion of a single drivin
wheel tender engine in the face of increasingly heavy main line trains an
went for a large boilered 'simple' 4-4-0. As in virtually all his subsequen
designs inside Stephenson's link gear was employed. One feature that wa
carried over, however, from his brother's era was the outside valve chests a
used on the class 'J' compound singles. With 19ins. by 26ins. cylinders an
7ft. 1ins. driving wheels the 'M1' engines were most imposing and ver
handsome retaining the established NER cab and driving wheel splasher
Twenty were built at Gateshead between 1892 and March 1894, the last o
the class No 1639 being experimentally fitted with piston valves, one o
the first NER locomotives to be so treated.

Prior to the indroduction of this class the heaviest trains on the East Coas
line had had to be double headed, particularly between Newcastle an
Edinburgh, and often by a combination of a single wheeler and a fou

ɔupled engine. The 'M1s', however, could tackle normal loads on the ɔute single handed. The class was to achieve celebrity for the role it ayed in the 1895 'Race to Aberdeen' albeit in conjunction with William ʼorsdell's 'J' class engines. These latter were rebuilt by Wilson in 1894/95 s described earlier as 'simple' engines with Stephenson link gear and Ʋalter Smith's Patent Piston Valves. In this form their performance was ery much improved and notwithstanding the 'M1s', they were still to a ɪrge extent the pride of the line. Both classes featured prominently in the ß95 'Races', fought between the same groups of companies as the 'Race ▸ Edinburgh' seven years previously. Generally speaking throughout July ɪnd August of 1895 the East Coast route 'racing train' (which left London ɪings Cross at 8pm) was hauled over NER metals by a rebuilt 'J' class ɪgine from York to Newcastle and thence to Edinburgh over the more ɪeeply graded section by an 'M1'. At the end of August when rivalry ɪtween the two routes became really intense the time for the 80.6 miles ɔm York to Newcastle was reduced from 92 to 80 minutes. At this point

ilson Worsdell's first major design for the NER was the 'M1' class. These ɪgines are famous for their role in the 'Races to Aberdeen' in 1895. One of the ɪe involved, No. 1621, is preserved at the National Railway Museum, but the ɪss is represented here by No. 1630.   *(K. Hoole collection, per K. Taylor)*

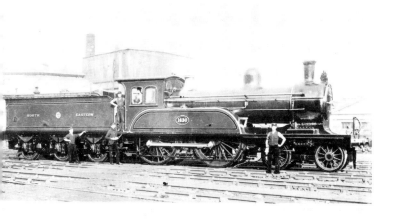

'M1' class engines were introduced on this leg of the journey als[o]
displacing the 'Js' which had performed admirably to the old schedu[le]
with loads of around 200 tons.

The climax was reached over the night of the 21st/22nd August. 'N[o]
No. 1621 had charge of the train and covered the York to Newcastle sectio[n]
in 78½ minutes at an average speed of 61½ mph. Another engine of th[e]
same class No 1620 took over the 105 ton train and covered the 124.4 mil[es]
to Edinburgh in a probable time of 113 minutes, an average speed of [6]
mph and a record thought by more than one author never to have bee[n]
bettered in the days of steam. The train taken on from Edinburgh by t[he]
North British Railway arrived at Aberdeen on this occasion at 04.40 hou[rs]
one hour ahead of schedule. A distance of 523½ miles had been covered [in]
520 minutes including stoppages. The following night the West Coa[st]
route companies retaliated with an exhibition run, albeit with a train
only 65 tons, covering the 540 miles on their route to Aberdeen in only 5[12]
minutes. Honour perhaps having been satisfied the 1895 'Races' ende[d]
rather indecisively at this point. Fortunately one of the NER engin[es]
involved in these historic events has survived, No. 1621 occupying a pla[ce]
of honour in the National Railway Museum at York.

Whilst he was later to become noted for his rejection of the use [of]
compounding on the NER Wilson did not in fact dismiss the principle o[ut]
of hand. A two cylinder compound version of the 'M1' class was produc[ed]
in May 1893 emerging very soon after the first 'M1s' had been put to wor[k]
This was the 'M' class engine, No. 1619, built with high and low pressu[re]
cylinders of 19ins. and 28ins. diameter respectively and with a stroke [of]
26ins. His brother's favoured Joy valve gear was replaced by Stephens[on]
link motion and the engine operated at 200lbs per square inch boil[er]
pressure as against the 180lbs of its 'simple' sisters. In this form No. 16[19]
seems to have performed very well reportedly using some 10% less fu[el]
than the orthodox engines. Despite this, however, Wilson pressed ahe[ad]
with the conversion of many of William's compound designs to simp[le]
operation, notably the 'J' class 4-2-2s and 'C' class 0-6-0s from 1894. [He]
also put in hand new construction of some of his brother's non-compou[nd]
types such as the 'C1' 0-6-0s. In view of all this it is perhaps surprising th[at]
in 1898 when No. 1619 was rebuilt it again appeared as a compound, t[his]
time, however with three cylinders, one at high pressure between t[he]
frames and two at low pressure outside. Much of the credit for this desi[gn]
has been given to Walter Smith. Smith had been a one-time colleague [of]
Samuel Waite Johnson at this period locomotive superintendent of t[he]
Midland Railway and had developed his piston valves at Gateshead [in]

122

conjunction with that company's engineers at Derby.

In its new guise No. 1619 had LP cylinders of 24ins. stroke and an HP cylinder of 26ins. stroke. A much larger boiler was provided but design constraints resulted in a long, shallow firebox unlike those normally provided on the NER. Perhaps for this reason No. 1619 does not seem to have been notably successful in this form, a fact which could have done nothing to enhance Wilson's view of compounding. Indeed only two more compound locomotives were to be constructed for the company during his period in office. However, the rebuilding of No. 1619 did mark a very significant point in locomotive design if not for the North Eastern,since there is no doubt that Smith's work inspired his friends at Derby to produce the famous 'Midland compounds' built to the same configuration from 1902. The Great Central Railway also introduced the type with success but it is on the Midland Railway that 'Smith Compounds' achieved such outstanding prominence no less than 240 being built for express passenger work by that company and its successor the London Midland and Scottish Railway.

n 'N' class tank engine photographed in LNER livery at York in 1928.
(P. Ransome-Wallis collection/NRM, York)

Wilson, however, was not lured down this path and with the exceptions referred to above all his future designs were to be 'simple' types. His 'N' class tank locomotives of 1893 were a very prosaic return to earth after the glamorous 'M/M1' design. An 0-6-2 type they were very similar to his brother's 'B1s' of 1886 but with larger cylinders and, of course, Stephenson link motion. Twenty engines were built at Darlington in 1893 and 1894 becoming LNER class 'N9' and a few survived into the 1950s in British Railways ownership.

Wilson's 'O' class of 1894 was a rather more significant design and one which inspired much affection being found in latter years on branch line work throughout the North Eastern system. They have been said to have been one of the most successful tank engines of the 0-4-4 wheel arrangement ever to run in Britain. Intended for short distance and branch line passenger trains they were natural competitors to William Worsdell's 'A' class 2-4-2s being of very similar dimensions. Although there is a good engineering reason, concerned with weight distribiution, to prefer the 0-4-4

The 'O' class were successful and long-lived branch line engines. This interesting view of LNER No. 1882 shows the type far from its native heath at Seven Sisters in North London in 1939 on a shuttle train to Palace Gates.

(P. Ransome-Wallis collection/NRM, York

side tank arrangement to that of 2-4-2, except where very high speed running is involved, it is tempting to speculate that Wilson was asserting his independence from his brother's ideas yet again in this case.

No less than 110 of these engines were built between 1894 and 1901, all at Darlington, and initially they tended to replace 0-4-4 well tanks designed by Edward Fletcher in the 1870s. Their success can be judged by the fact as class 'G5' most survived beyond nationalisation in 1948, and indeed on many duties were never superceded by modern steam locomotives, giving way only to diesel multiple units in the late 1950s.

Ever since the end of Fletcher's superintendency there had been great emphasis at Gateshead on standardisation and the interchangeability of parts in the locomotive department as a means of cutting costs. In the series of freight locomotives designed from 1894 onwards however this objective seems to have been lost sight of. The NER was always a freight carrier above all, its very origins being in the early tramroads and railways bringing coal from the hinterland of Durham to the ports and river wharves. The railway developed with the growth of the coal industry and of iron and steel in centres such as Middlesborough, Hartlepool and Consett throughout the second half of the 19th century and until 1914. There was always a need for robust, powerful six wheeled freight engines to cope with this staple traffic and in 1894 Wilson Worsdell introduced the 'P' class and later in 1898 a variant classified 'P1'. In these designs however Wilson produced engines very similar to his brother's 'C1' type and it is hard to see the logic in the multiplicity of types thus arrived at. Admittedly each design was more powerful than its predecessor, reflecting perhaps the buoyancy of traffic in the 1890s, but the difference was very marginal and any operating benefits must have been vitiated by the engineering maintenance implications of this proliferation.

Seventy class 'P' engines were built from 1894 to 1898 and 140 'P1s' between 1898 and 1903 both largely at Gateshead. They were reliable if unglamorous machines and like many Worsdell freight engines had long lives becoming LNER classes 'J24' and 'J25'. A few 'J24s' and most of the 'J25s' survived to be nationalised on January 1st 1948 and some of the latter survived into the early 1960s on humble freight duties notably around Gateshead, Tyne Dock and Sunderland. Whilst discussing six coupled freight engines it is perhaps worth abandoning the chronological treatment of Wilson's designs to discuss classes 'P2' and 'P3' which brought yet further diversity to the NER 0-6-0 fleet. These engines came about as one result of the findings of a visit of senior NER officers, including Wilson, to study railway operation in the United States in October 1901.

The 'P' class of 1894 were the first of Wilson Worsdell's successful six-coupled tender designs. Here in LNER days No. 1897D completes a lovely period view well outside NER territory at Inverkeithing. *(R. D. Stephen collection/NRM, York)*

'P1' class No. 2055 darkens the sky at the head of an up goods train at Low Fell,
Gateshead. *(K. Taylor collection)*

One strong message they brought back was the need to increase train loads
and decrease train mileage. In order to implement this objective mineral
wagons of various sizes: 15, 20, 32 and even 40 tons were tested as
alternatives to the existing eight and 10½ ton vehicles before the 20 ton
wagon was finally decided upon in 1903. The introduction of railway
owned 20 ton wagons, intensively used, running perhaps two or three
round trips per day, in place of an assortment of small privately owned
wagons running low mileages, and in conjunction with excellent freight
locomotives, put the NER in the Wilson Worsdell era in a supreme position
as regards minerals handling. The North East maintained this supremacy
for 50 years throughout the LNER period and into nationalisation.

The 'T1' 0-8-0s, of which more later, had been introduced in 1901 and
would clearly see great use on the much heavier trains envisaged but the
need for a much larger 0-6-0 was also perceived. The 'P2' locomotives that
resulted in 1904 could never be confused with their predecessor 0-6-0s.
Though having the same size cylinders as the 'P1s' they had massive
boilers, the largest seen to date on engines of the type in Britain. The larger

127

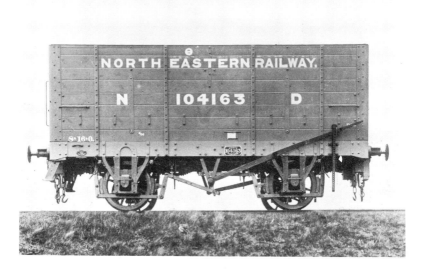

The standard 20-ton coal wagon of 1906, intensively used, exemplified the pre-eminence of the NER in bulk mineral haulage during the Wilson Worsdell era and for many years afterwards. *(By courtesy of the National Railway Museum, York)*

firebox grate area and increased adhesive weight gave rise to an engine that steamed freely and was a surefooted and strong puller. The overall impression was of an engine a 'size bigger' than the 'C1s' and 'Ps'. These fine machines were intended exclusively for freight working being fitted only with steam brakes and worked heavy long distance mineral trains and main line freight traffic. 50 were built by 1905, 20 at Gateshead and the other 30 at the newly expanded Darlington works. As originally built the 'P2s' were fitted with boilers working at a pressure of 200lbs per square inch. From 1906 further engines were built with this pressure reduced to 180lbs but with the cylinder diameter increased fractionally to 18½ins. Virtually indistinguishable from their sisters these engines were designated 'P3'. 80 of this type were constructed starting in 1906 and so successful were they that a further 35 appeared from Darlington from 1921 fitted with piston valves and superheaters. The last ten of these engines actually appeared after the grouping under LNER auspices in 1923.

The 'P2s' and 'P3s' were outstandingly successful locomotives by any

Wilson Worsdell's very powerful 'P2' and 'P3' engines helped to place the NER at the forefront of mineral traffic practice from the early years of the 20th century. These locos were so successful that they survived to the end of steam in the North East. 'P3' No. 1402 illustrates these fine machines. *(K. Taylor collection)*

yardstick. Redesignated 'J26' and 'J27' respectively by the LNER all of them were taken into British Railways ownership and continued to do excellent work in the North East notably at Blyth and Sunderland until the very end of steam in that region, outlasting many modern engines built as late as the 1950s. The last five 'J27s' were taken out of service in September 1967. One of these, NER No. 2360, latterly British Railways No. 65882, was actually the last NER locomotive to remain in operation and the last pre-grouping standard gauge engine working in Britain.

Appropriately another of the five has survived in preservation to commemorate Wilson Worsdell's splendid design. This is NER No. 2392, No. 65894 on British Railways, and the last one constructed at Darlington in 1923. Owned by the North Eastern Locomotive Preservation Group the engine is maintained in immaculate order and is usually to be found on the North Yorkshire Moors Railway.

The 'Q' class which appeared in 1896 hardly justified its separate designation being very similar to the 'M1' class 4-4-0s of four years earlier

The handsome 'Q' class of 1896 were very similar to the earlier 'M' class engines. This fine shot shows No. 1871 complete with brass-rimmed chimney and clerestory roofed cab at St. Margarets, Edinburgh, in the late 1890s. *(G. Tod collection/NRM, York)*

but having a slightly smaller boiler and smokebox (which improved their appearance) and inside valve chests. Uniquely amongst North Eastern engines the 'Q' class and the derivative 'Q1s' had driving cabs ventilated by clerestories. By way of decoration Wilson fitted brass rims to their chimneys a feature that his brother would no doubt have applauded. 30 engines were built at Gateshead in 1896-97 and like their 'cousins' the 'M1s' they performed very satisfactorily as well as being very good looking. They were destined to be long lived compared with most express passenger types lasting well into LNER days as class 'D17/2'. Used when new on the 'Flying Scotsman' and on the night Aberdeen express, which included a fast 92 minute schedule between York and Newcastle, they were still to be found working on secondary lines as late as 1938.

Two locomotives constructed just before the first 'Q' made its appearance were designated 'Q1'. Although there were other detailed differences they were essentially a class 'Q' with the coupled wheel diameter increased from 7ft. 1ins. to 7ft. 7ins. Wilson thus earned the

No. 1869 was one of two 'Q' class engines built with 7ft. 7in. driving wheels overtly as 'racing machines'. *(K. Taylor collection)*

accolade of having designed the locomotives with the largest coupled wheels ever to run in Britain. It must be remembered that they appeared only one year after the 1895 'Race to Aberdeen'. It is generally agreed that the two engines, which actually emerged from Gateshead Works in May and June of 1896, were produced solely to ensure that the NER would be well placed should another outbreak of 'racing' occur. This in fact never happened and the two engines, Nos 1869 and 1870 were used interchangeably with the 'Q' class engines. Perhaps surprisingly for non-standard engines, they survived for 34 years being honoured with the separate classification 'D18' by the LNER.

Only three 'H2' class engines were built. Number 1787 pauses between shunting duties at York in 1901. *(K. Taylor collection)*

Class 'H2' appeared in 1897 an insignificant class in every way. Only three were built and they were small shunting engines dimensionally similar to William Worsdell's 'H1s' but without the jib-crane. They were classified 'J79' by the LNER.

Wilson's next design class 'E1' was a neat little six wheeled tank engine for shunting and light goods duties. With 17ins. by 24ins. cylinders and wheels of only 4ft. 1ins. diameter they were quite powerful little engines. They had a most unusual construction history. Seventy-five of the type were built at Darlington and by outside contractors up to 1921 under Wilson and his successor Vincent Raven; another ten were constructed by the LNER in 1925 at the former Great Northern Railway workshops at Doncaster and astonishingly another 28 by British Railways at Darlington between 1949 and 1951. The extraordinary decision of the nationalised undertaking to dust off the drawings of a 50 year old design and construct more is the best possible testimony to the excellence of Wilson Worsdell's engines. One of the post-nationalisation members of class 'J72', as they became, No. 69023 has survived in preservation and after several changes of ownership can now be found operating in appropriate surroundings on the North Yorkshire Moors Railway. Two others, British Railways Nos 68723 and 68736, achieved celebrity in the late 1950s, in the manner of the 'E' class engine previously mentioned, being turned out in NER light

The 'E1' class engines were remarkable in that successive batches were constructed over a period of more than 50 years, an outstanding tribute to Wilson Worsdell's design. *(K. Taylor collection)*

green livery (instead of the usual BR black) for shunting duties at York and Newcastle stations. All of the original engines survived to rub shoulders with the post-nationalisation examples and were only replaced by diesel shunters in the late 1950s and early 1960s.

By 1899 the NER required a slightly larger express passenger engine than the 'M1' and 'Q' classes to avoid the need for doubleheading and to fill this gap Wilson produced his 'R' class 4-4-0s. Apart from having a larger boiler and slightly smaller driving wheels at 6ft. 10ins., the main difference lay in the provision of piston valves of Walter Smith's patent design. They proved to be splendid engines, economical and very reliable in service. The first of the type No. 2011 was at the outset diagrammed to run from Newcastle to Edinburgh and back and then to Leeds and back each day. Moreover the engine is said to have kept this up six days a week for over two years clocking up an incredible 248,000 miles before its first general overhaul. Even in recent years British Railways steam locomotives did

The 'R' class of 1899 were undoubtedly one of the finest Worsdell designs. Here No. 2019 makes a superb sight crossing the High Level Bridge at Newcastle.
(By courtesy of the National Railway Museum, York)

very well to average 100,000 miles between overhauls so No. 2011's reported performance was either very remarkable indeed or needed to be taken with a large pinch of salt!

Another member of the class for many years held the speed record for the Darlington to York run, No. 1672 covering the 44.1 miles in 39 minutes 34 seconds with a load of 165 tons. Thirty of the class were constructed at Gateshead in three batches of ten by 1901. So successful were they judged to be that a further 30 were built, also at Gateshead, in 1906-1907. They gave years of excellent service many still being active as 'D20s', albeit on

Another 'R' class engine, as British Railways 62395, was photographed at Darlington in 1957, soon before being scrapped.
(By courtesy of the National Railway Museum, York)

less exacting duties, in the 1950s notably in the Selby and Hull areas and at Tweedmouth, Regrettably they did not quite last into the 'preservation era' and all had been scrapped by 1958.

The next design from the Gateshead drawing office was another landmark in locomotive practice. With his 'S' class Wilson was the first to

The 'S' class engines were the first express passenger 4-6-0s in Britain, though they must be judged only moderately successful. LNER No. 1699 illustrates the class.
(N. E. Stead collection)

use the 4-6-0 wheel arrangement for a British express passenger engine. This type had already been used successfully in the United States for some years and it has been suggested that Wilson's youthful experience in that country disposed him to take notice of developments there. The first of the class No. 2001 emerged from Gateshead works in 1899. The coupled wheels were of 6ft. 1ins. diameter and the boiler was not overlarge. Today we would describe the class as a 'mixed traffic' type suitable for express freight work but not for the fastest passenger trains. Together the engine and tender weighed 105 tons being the largest seen at that time in Britain. The prototype engine was given a very severe trial on a test run from Newcastle to Edinburgh. Hauling twenty five vehicles with a combined weight of 352 tons an average speed in the upper forties only was achieved which appeared to indicate that whatever their other qualities they would never be 'fliers'.

This realisation prompted the development of the 'S1' which first appeared in 1901. Here the driving wheel diameter was increased to 6ft. 8ins. with a consequent increase in wheelbase and a longer boiler was fitted. Piston valves were also employed. In practise the new engines were

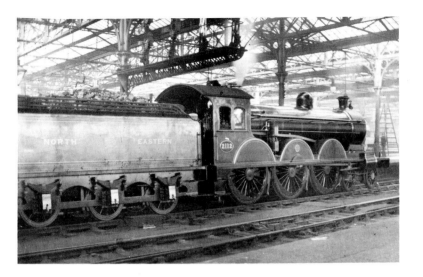

This photograph of 'S1' class No. 2112 under the train shed at Newcastle Central clearly shows the 'high stepping' appearance given by the 6ft. 8in. driving wheels. *(K. Taylor collection)*

no improvement on the 'R' class 4-4-0s on express trains and were more expensive to operate. As a result no more than the original batch of five ever appeared. They became the LNER's 'B14' class but were not to be long lived.

The 'S' class engines however evidently found their niche amongst the locomotive fleet no less than 40 being built in total in two batches, ten in 1899-1900 and the other 30 from Gateshead in 1906-09 with various modifications such as the substitution of piston valves for slide valves. Wilson fitted the last twenty of the class (and also the later 'W' and 'R1' locomotives) with a variable blastpipe and ash ejector. This device was jointly patented by Wilson and Mr W. R. Preston of Messrs J. Stone and Co. Ltd of Deptford in 1907 (Patent No. 16,980). It enabled the driver to reduce the draught on the fire by increasing the blastpipe diameter when the engine was working hard, thus reducing fire loss through the chimney, and also prevented ash accumulation in the smokebox by ejecting it through the chimney. It is said that the latter function resulted in lineside crops being set on fire rather too often and probably explains why this interesting innovation was removed from all types of engine from 1910.

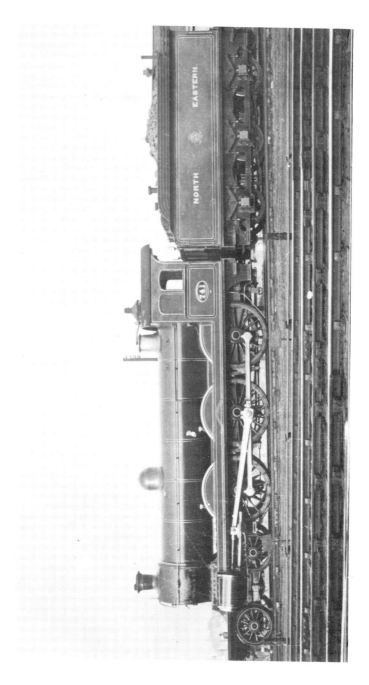

(*K. Taylor collection*)

Another 'S' class engine, No. 741.

One of the first batch of the class, No. 2006, was sent to the Paris Exhibition of 1900 and obtained celebrity by winning a gold medal, copies of which were carried on the driving wheel splashers. This engine on its return to England also ran experimentally as an oil burner for some time. Leaving aside the Paris success and the occasional Royal Train duty the engines led a rather unglamorous existence as mixed traffic engines despite their handsome and imposing appearance. Classified 'B13' by the LNER they began to be taken out of service by 1928 and few survived until 1939, although one example, No. 761, was used for many years in conjunction with the locomotive testing dynamometer car train (q.v.) and lasted until about 1951 in British Railways ownership.

The '290' class 0-6-0 tank engines also appeared first in 1899. They were so designated, and not by letter, presumably because they were considered rebuilds rather than new engines. Wilson notionally used the boiler, cylinders and motion of the 'BTP' class 0-4-4 tank engines, which had been superceded by the 'O' class, as the basis of the 'new' locomotives. Intended for shunting work the '290s' had 17ins. by 22ins. cylinders and driving wheels of 4ft. 1ins. diameter. Forty were constructed/rebuilt at York up to 1904 and the other 20 in two batches of ten at Darlington, in 1907/08 and in 1921, after the closure of the York works. Redesignated 'J77' by the LNER a few were taken out of service in the 1930s but the majority survived to be nationalised in 1948. More than

The '290' class first appeared in 1899 and were rebuilds of earlier engines. They were very successful and long-lived. Number 1439 was photographed at Ardsley, near Leeds in 1938. *(J. P. Mullett collection/NRM, York)*

half of these tough little engines were still working in 1953 and they did yeoman service pushing loaded coal hopper wagons up on to the coal staithes at the docks at North and South Blyth.

Even before the 'large wagon/increased train pay load' policy was adopted following the senior officers' visit to the USA, freight trains had been steadily growing in size with the growth of the local economy in the North East. Wilson decided that an eight coupled locomotive would be required on the NER for the first time. His design was quite innovative in that unusually for this railway outside cylinders were employed, as with the 'S' class, and adhesive weight was maximised by an 0-8-0 configuration rather than the later standard for most railways, the 2-8-0. The cylinders were 20ins. in diameter by 26ins. stroke and with tender the

Eight-coupled goods engines were deemed necessary with the growth of both wagon size and payload on NER mineral trains in the early years of the century. Here No. 162 of the 'T' class heads a test train of 40-ton hopper wagons at Bootham Junction, York. *(By courtesy of the National Railway Museum, York)*

locomotive weighed nearly 97 tons. Initially ten engines fitted with Smith's piston valves were turned out by Gateshead works from August 1901 but these were followed by another ten built with slide valves between March and June 1902. The former were designated class 'T', the latter 'T1'. These locomotives were designed to haul trains of 60 loaded wagons (of 10½ tons each) but they proved so successful in traffic that the limit was increased to 72 and one engine on test at Tyne Dock hauled a train of no less than 1,326 tons. Other sterling work was performed by the

The 'T1' class engines were built with slide valves rather than the piston valves of class 'T'. Here No. 578D poses in immaculate condition at Selby in 1925.

(P. Ransome-Wallis collection/NRM, York)

class over the spectacular and steeply graded Stainmore route between West Auckland and the London and North Western Railway junction at Tebay.

By 1906 40 'T' class and ten 'T1s' were in service, all built at Gateshead. Comparative tests involving the two types were carried out in that year over the Stainmore route. They performed equally well on the track but rather surprisingly perhaps, in view of the opposite conclusion drawn from similar tests on the 'M1' class some years before, the slide valve engines used 10% less coal than the piston valve engines, a considerable saving. Thereafter only 'T1s' were built, another 40 appearing from Darlington this time, in 1907/08 and 1911. The 50 'T1s' were notable in being sent to

Many of the Worsdell eight wheelers were 'called up' during the First World War and did valuable work on supply trains behind the allied lines in France. Number 660 is shown here in the camouflaged disguise of No. 5660 of the Army's Railway Operating Division. *(By courtesy of the National Railway Museum, York)*

France during the First World War as part of the NER's contribution to the war effort. Used by the Army's Railway Operating Division on supply trains they won high praise for their power and reliability.

The engines of both sub-classes proved to be very fine machines and were grouped together as class 'Q5' by the LNER. Although these particular locomotives did not have notably long lives the outside cylinder 0-8-0 tender engine was to remain a stalwart part of the North Eastern scene until the demise of steam in that area in September 1967. Wilson's successor Vincent Raven developed the design during his period of office, a slightly larger, superheated version (NER class 'T2', LNER 'Q6') appearing in 1913. 120 of these had been built by 1921. Finally in 1919 the peak of NER freight engine design was reached with a yet further enlargement of the concept the result being an engine with three cylinders of 18ins. by 26ins. and with a very large boiler. These 'T3s' were, in effect, about 15% bigger than the 'T2s' and, incidentally, much better looking. They spent their later years (as LNER 'Q7s') working iron ore trains from Tyne Dock to Consett iron and steel works. The first 'T3' (NER No. 901, British Railways 63460) has been preserved as part of the National Collection of historic locomotives, whilst 'T2' No. 2238 (British Railways 63395), the last survivor of the class, was acquired in 1967 by the North Eastern Locomotive Preservation Group. Both can be seen on the North Yorkshire Moors Railway reminding us of a noble lineage of eight-wheelers conceived by Wilson Worsdell.

The 'U' class 0-6-2 tank engines first appeared in 1902 in which year Wilson's title was changed from Locomotive Superintendent to Chief Mechanical Engineer. Very similar to the 'N' class of 1893 but with piston valves and smaller wheels the 'Us' were intended primarily for freight traffic. Twenty were built at Darlington in 1902-03 and all survived into the

This sturdy 'U' class tank engine, designed for shunting and goods work was one of twenty built and was photographed at Dairycoates (Hull) in July 1936.

(J. P. Mullett collection/NRM, York)

1950s having been classified 'N10' by the LNER. The last survivors in the early 1960s were based at Bowes Bridge and worked coal trains over the Tanfield Branch in West Durham.

Wilson's next design the 'V' class of 1903 with the 'Atlantic' or 4-4-2 wheel arrangement also owed much to the 1901 American visit. The 'R' class engines were the top NER express locomotives at the time but a larger engine was coming to be required and with a better turn of speed than the 'S' class 4-6-0s. Whilst in the USA the NER party travelled in excess of 4,500 miles, over the main railway systems of that country. One of the lines visited was the Philadelphia and Reading Railroad then operating the fastest trains in the USA, the 'Atlantic City Fliers'. An account of this visit published in the *Locomotive Magazine* of 10th January 1903 suggests that Wilson was not privileged to see or travel on these trains having been left ill at Chicago. However, his colleagues could not fail to be impressed with what they saw. The 'Fliers' were scheduled to cover the 55½ miles from Camden to Atlantic City in 50 minutes at an average speed of 66.6 miles per hour with a load of between 200 and 300 tons. On the day of the visit the journey was accomplished in 46½ minutes (71.6 miles per hour average), the fastest mile being covered at 85.1 mph and an astonishing average of 81.5 mph being maintained over 35 consecutive miles. The locomotive was a four cylinder compound 'Atlantic' and the North Eastern men commented on the wonderful smoothness of the running at high speeds. Their reports must have impressed Wilson to the extent that he resolved to build similar large boilered 'Atlantics' for the North Eastern. Engine No. 532 emerged from Gateshead works on 3rd November 1903. Weighing 72 tons without tender it was the largest engine to that date owned by the company and outsized the celebrated Great Northern Railway 'Atlantics' of 1902. Number 532 had two outside cylinders of 20ins. diameter and 28ins. stroke, (Wilson predictably rejected compounding), driving wheels of 6ft. 10ins. diameter and a boiler of 5ft. 6ins. diameter, the overall impression being of a massive but certainly not ungainly machine.

Ten engines of the class were built at Gateshead in 1903-04 but though capable of hard work they must be deemed as rather a disappointment, the engines in practise not being notably superior to the splendid 'R' class 4-4-0s which continued to work many of the most important expresses. The relative failure of the 'Atlantics' has been put down to deficiencies in the design of the piston valves which failed to allow sufficient steam to enter the cylinders. This problem was overcome in the design of the later 'Atlantics', the 'V1s' of 1910 of which more later.

The 'V' class 'Atlantics' of 1903 were inspired by contemporary American practice. Though not in terms of performance a great advance on the 'R' class 4-4-0s, they were very striking in appearance as this 1924 view of the prototype No. 532 at York illustrates. *(P. Ransome-Wallis collection/NRM, York)*

Though largely displaced from the most important trains, by Vincent Raven's 'Z' class three cylinder 'Atlantics' from 1911 the 'Vs' did useful work over many years. Most survived until the Second World War as LNER class 'C6' and, given a reprieve by that emergency, some saw out the war based at Darlington depot.

It is said that Walter Smith, the Chief Draughtsman at Gateshead and proponent of compounding, was not entirely pleased with the design of the 'V' class which occured largely in his absence through illness. There is no doubt, however, that the next 'Atlantic' design owed much to his ideas. The '4CC' class engines were as their name suggests, four cylinder compounds. They had high pressure cylinders of 14½ins. diameter outside the frames, and low pressure cylinders of 22ins. diameter inside. The boiler was smaller than on the 'Vs' and, uniquely on the NER, but reflecting Smith's Derby connections, a Belpaire firebox was employed. Only two engines of the type were constructed, Nos. 730 and 731, and the second of

Only two of these four-cylinder compound '4cc' engines were built, representing a very unusual diversion from NER practice of the time. They were, however, very successful and long-lived for a non-standard type. This fine view shows No. 730 at York in 1927.

(P. Ransome-Wallis collection/NRM, York)

these was also unusual in being the only NER locomotive to have Walschaerts valve gear. Quite what Wilson Worsdell made of it all is not absolutely clear given his antipathy to his brother's earlier compounding ideas, but there is no doubt that these two locomotives performed outstandingly, though Walter Smith never lived to see this, dying soon after their completion. As an example of their work when nearly new in 1906, No. 730 hauling a 455 ton train covered the 44.1 miles between Darlington and York in 45½ minutes.

Also in 1906 a detailed series of tests were carried out using the dynamometer car (described later) to compare the performance of the 'R', 'S1', 'V' and '4CC' classes. The '4CC' emerged very well from these, out-performing the 'S1' and 'V' broadly speaking, but not representing any significant improvement on the excellent 'R' class. Neither were any operating economies, such as in coal consumption, identified to offset the higher construction and maintenance costs. The result was that the compound design, though an excellent one, was not proceeded with and

An 'official' NER photograph taken at Jarrow Slake of the 'W' class locomotive No. 686. These engines were designed for passenger work on the Scarborough to Saltburn coastal route. *(By courtesy of the National Railway Museum, York)*

no more were built. Perhaps Wilson's views were vindicated after all. The '4CCs' (along with the 'R' & 'V' classes) were superseded as top rank express engines with the introduction of the 'Z' class in 1911 but nevertheless survived in LNER ownership until the mid-1930s being reclassified as the 'C8s'.

The 'W' class was Wilson's next design and was very much a 'one-off', being intended for passenger service on the switchback gradients of the Scarborough-Whitby-Saltburn line where the 'O' class 0-4-4 tanks were found increasingly unsatisfactory. A six coupled engine was clearly desirable to increase adhesive weight but surprisingly Wilson settled on an inside cylinder 4-6-0 tank engine configuration, a most unusual if not unique type. Ten were built in 1907-08 with 19ins. by 26ins. cylinders and with a total weight of 69 tons they were quite large engines. In service the 'Ws' were found to carry insufficient coal and this led to them being rebuilt after a few years with an extended bunker supported by a trailing axle. In

The 'R1' class of 1908 was an attempt to improve further the successful 'R' class with the addition of a larger boiler. This view of No. 1244, taken at Low Fell, illustrates the impressive dimensions of the type.   *(K. Taylor collection)*

this form some of the engines, reclassified 'W1', survived into the early 1950s as LNER class 'A6', but they never succeeded in completely replacing the 'O' class engines in their intended area of operation and must be considered rather nondescript by Wilson's normal standards.

Increasing train size ensured that there was always a need for yet larger passenger engines on the NER so it was not perhaps surprising that following the comparative tests between 'R', 'S1' and 'V' classes Wilson should hit upon the idea of improving the extremely successful 'R' class engines by the addition of a larger boiler. The 'R1' class of 1908 comprised in effect a shortened large diameter boiler from the 'V' class (operating at the high pressure of 225lbs per square inch) fitted to an 'R' class 4-4-0 chassis. The result was a heavy engine with 21 tons adhesive weight on each axle. Clearly the 'R1s' were going to be 'sure footed' machines but there was a fundamental design fault in the firebox provided which resulted in very high coal consumption. This made them unpopular with footplate crews and accountants alike. Only ten were built, at Darlington in 1908-09, and although they did some good work in their early years between Newcastle and Edinburgh, the design was not persevered with and Wilson returned to the 'Atlantic' type for his main express passenger engines. As a numerically small, non-standard class the 'R1s' were, unsurprisingly, taken out of service long before their successful and more numerous cousins the 'R' class.

The 'X' class engines which first appeared in 1909 were a novel departure from the mainstream of locomotive design. At this time the NER was constructing a very large marshalling yard at Middlesbrough. This was to be called the Erimus yard and was to be worked on the 'hump' principle. Clearly very powerful shunting engines would be required to push trains of loaded wagons up the hump and for this purpose Wilson designed a 4-8-0 tank locomotive. The three cylinders, all contained in a single casting foreshadowing the type of construction used later by the LNER's Nigel Gresley, made it very unlikely that these engines would ever stall whilst working at low speed up the hump and the 85 tons weight guaranteed good adhesion. Rather curiously the inside cylinder drove the first coupled axle whilst the outside pair drove the second pair of wheels via a long connecting rod. Ten members of class 'X' appeared from Gateshead works in 1909-10 and with their 18ins. by 26ins. cylinders and 4ft. 7¼ins. driving wheels they proved ideal for the work at the Erimus yard and at Hull and other freight marshalling centres. These engines were the last to be built at the cramped and restricted site at Gateshead, all new construction thereafter being concentrated at the Darlington works where facilities had

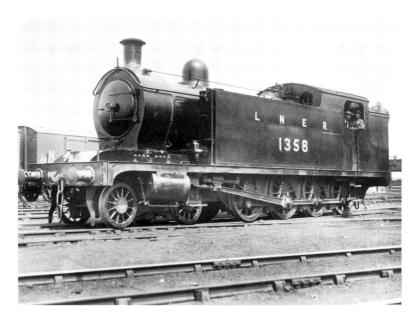

The three-cylindered 'X' class were built for heavy shunting work in marshalling yards and were the last engines built in the old works at Gateshead. Here a shining No. 1358 again testifies to the pride of the staff at Selby in the late 1920s. *(P. Ransome-Wallis collection/NRM, York)*

been greatly expanded over the years. A further five 'Xs' were built at Darlington in late 1925 and these were the last engines built there for the LNER of North Eastern design. Thirteen members of the class survived into nationalisation having been designated 'T1' by the LNER. They were finally displaced from their duties by diesel shunters in the late 1950s.

Wilson's last locomotive design was the 'V1' an 'Atlantic' developed from the 'V' class of 1903. The design deficiencies of the latter have been alluded to earlier and the aim was to eliminate these in the new engines. The piston valves were modified to allow a sufficiency of steam to enter the cylinders under normal operating conditions and the smokebox was redesigned and extended for better performance and appearance. A reduction in cylinder diameter to 19½ins. and in boiler pressure to 180 lbs per square inch resulted in a locomotive nominally less powerful than its precursor and also the recently constructed 'R1s'. Nevertheless they were fast, free running engines if somewhat underpowered for heavy work on steep gradients. The first two engines of the class appeared from Darlington

150

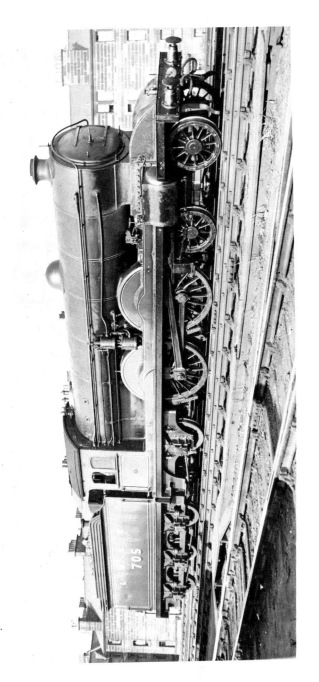

The 'V1' 'Atlantics' appeared in 1910 incorporating a number of improvements to the 'V' class and were to be Wilson Worsdell's last design before retirement. Number 705 reflects great credit to its designer in this shot taken at Gorgie, near Edinburgh.

(R. D. Stephen collection/NRM, York)

Works at about the time of Wilson's retirement at the end of May 1910 and no more than ten were ever built. This can be attributed to the influence of Vincent Raven who succeeded Wilson as Chief Mechanical Engineer having been his Chief Assistant for more than 15 years. Seeking an improvement to the somewhat disappointing 'V' and 'R1' engines, Raven decided to introduce a three cylinder 'Atlantic' which was to become the 'Z' class. These engines were an immediate success earning a reputation for fast, smooth running, the latter a result of the more even, continuous power output from the three cylinders. They were moreover substantially less heavy on coal than the two cylinder engines and ran greater mileages between repairs. The superiority of the 'Zs' was such that no less than 50 were built and no more two cylinder 'Atlantics' ever appeared. The 'V1s', however, were useful engines destined to survive for many years. They were classified together with 'V' class as LNER class 'C6' and the last member of that class survived literally to the very eve of nationalisation being taken out of service on 31st December 1947.

Despite holding very different views on locomotive design from his brother, Wilson Worsdell brought a similar concern for the highest standards to his work. His locomotives were not only, by and large, very sucessful, but they were also aesthetically very pleasing. The beautiful, ornately lined out livery applied to all engines by William was perpetuated for many years although eventually economy demanded a simpler, though still attractive, paint scheme for goods and shunting engines. It was only after Wilson's retirement and with the coming of war that an 'austerity' livery came to be introduced on these humbler engines, green paintwork giving way to black, and brass adornments largely disappearing.

Between the time of its incorporation in 1864 and 1914 the North Eastern Railway had experienced dynamic growth; Route mileage increased from just over 700 miles to about 1700 and total trackage including sidings tripled over the period at the end of which the company controlled no less than seventeen docks. Wilson Worsdell served the company through the core of this period from 1883 until his retirement in 1910. He is remembered for his locomotives but it should not be lost sight of that as Superintendent, and later as Chief Mechanical Engineer, he was responsible also for all passenger and goods rolling stock, the company's fleet of tugboats and for the hydraulic machinery used for the transhipment of coal at docks and staiths. His 'empire' was such that by 1903 there were some 18,500 people employed in his department and he was responsible for 2,142 locomotives, 4,000 passenger carriages and 98,000 goods wagons.

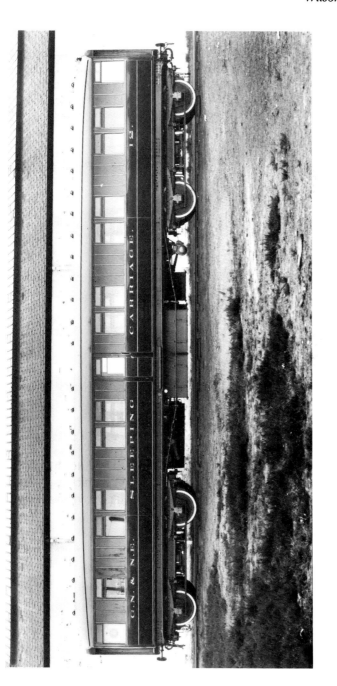

A sleeping car of the Great Northern and North Eastern Railways joint stock of the Wilson Worsdell era. These vehicles brought a new standard of comfort to the East Coast main line night trains. *(By courtesy of the National Railway Museum, York)*

The electrification of the North Tyneside suburban services in 1904 was another innovation during Wilson Worsdell's tenure. The third rail pick-up is prominent in this view of the new electric trains. *(By courtesy of the National Railway Museum, York)*

Wilson was very active in the field of passenger carriage design. On a railway historically oriented to the carriage of goods traffic he set new standards providing for the East Coast expresses vehicles of a degree of comfort hitherto unknown. He also introduced sleeping cars with transverse rather than longitudinal berths and with a separate compartment for each passenger.

He was prominently involved in the introduction of the latest forms of traction on the NER, notably with the electrification of the North Tyneside suburban services in 1904. This was promulgated largely to counter the success of the electric street tramways of the Newcastle area in attracting traffic previously carried by the railways. The lines chosen for electrification were those from Newcastle Central to North Shields and Tynemouth, Tynemouth to Newcastle via Whitley Bay and Backworth, and the Riverside loop via Walker. In all some 37 miles were involved, the current at 600 volts D.C. being conducted by the use of a third rail. These lines have had an interesting subsequent history. In the 1960s they were converted to diesel power as the then electrical equipment became obsolete and expensive to operate, only to be re-electrified in the late 1970s, this time with overhead pick-up, as part of the Tyne and Wear 'Metro' suburban railway network.

In conjunction with the original electrification scheme the goods only branch from Manors Station to Newcastle Quayside was also electrified. Two locomotives supplied by the Brush Electrical Engineering Company Limited for this line in 1902 were still at work there in the early 1960s. One, latterly British Railways No. 26500, has been preserved at the National Railway Museum at York serving as a tangible reminder of Wilson Worsdell's early involvement with railway electrification. Indeed this Tyneside scheme and the Lancashire and Yorkshire Railway's contemporary Liverpool to Southport and Crossens scheme were the first electrified suburban railways in Britain outside the London area.

Another innovation was the dynamometer car introduced in 1906 which was used to test many of Wilson's locomotives 'on the road' and which has been referred to earlier. Simply stated a dynamometer car, usually a converted passenger coach, is a vehicle containing instrumentation enabling the performance of a locomotive under test to be monitored. The data collected by such a car, most notably information on power output and speed on different gradients, when studied in conjunction with fuel consumption, provides valuable insight into operating economics. Wilson did not invent the dynamometer car but was responsible for its introduction on the NER. As recounted he had borrowed such a vehicle

The Dynamometer Car built in 1906 for testing locomotives 'on the road'. This vehicle registered the world speed record for steam traction when hauled by 'Mallard' in 1938 and is preserved at the National Railway Museum, York.

By courtesy of the National Railway Museum, York

from his friend George Jackson Churchward, the Chief Mechanical Engineer of the Great Western Railway, in 1903 in order to test his first 'V' class 'Atlantic', No. 532. So convinced was he of the value of the data collected that he constructed a very similar vehicle at York for the NER three years later. The North Eastern dynamometer car was to prove a very valuable piece of equipment and was, thanks to Wilson's generosity, sometimes loaned to other companies lacking such a car of their own. It eventually came into the ownership of the LNER and it was in this vehicle that the world speed record for steam traction, 126 miles per hour, was registered, on 2nd July 1938 when attached to the 'Pacific' locomotive 'Mallard'. Fortunately this historic vehicle, although considerably modified, can be seen (along with 'Mallard') at the National Railway Museum, York.

Mention of the York Museum provides an opportune moment to single out Wilson's contribution to the conservation of historic railway relics. The 'Billy', one of George Stephenson's early locomotives built for Springwell Colliery in 1826, had come into the custody of the NER in the early 1880s and had been set up in an exposed position at the north end of Newcastle's High Level Bridge. Wilson considered this very unsatisfactory and had it removed under cover at the city's Central Station. Later still, after his death, it was moved again to the Museum of Science and Industry on the Town Moor. Without Wilson's foresight this interesting relic might have crumbled to rust under the action of the Tyneside climate.

Inevitably, however, it is as a locomotive designer that we remember Wilson. In his twenty years in charge of locomotive matters, 1,002 engines were constructed at Gateshead and Darlington and some 200 of his brother William's compound locomotives were rebuilt as simple engines. Perhaps with hindsight we judge his 'R' class 4-4-0s, the 'P2' and 'P3' 0-6-0s and the 'T' 0-8-0s as his best engines but the imposing 'V' class 'Atlantics' and the innovatory 'S' class 4-6-0s have also helped to ensure Wilson Worsdell a secure place amongst the best British locomotive designers.

By the time of his retirement Wilson was responsible for a staff of nearly 20,000 including 4,000 on locomotive work at Gateshead and Darlington and 4,500 in the carriage and wagon shops at York. In addition to his locomotive work he had presided over the construction of 3,700 carriages and 96,500 wagons. One of his last innovations before retirement was to introduce the American practise of washing out locomotive boilers with hot water instead of cold. This simple expedient, as well as lessening the risk of damage to the firebox, reduced the time required to get up steam after washout from two hours to half an hour. Moreover, an engine on arrival at the depot could be made ready for washout in two hours as opposed to ten hours for a cold washout, a considerable saving in operating terms.

Wilson Worsdell was, as we would expect from his Quaker upbringing, a man with a strong sense of civic duty who took a great interest in the welfare of both his staff and the wider citizenry. During his time at Gateshead the working day for engine men was reduced to ten hours and extra payments for overtime and Sunday duty were introduced. As President of the North Eastern Literary Institute at Gateshead he did much to ensure success in its task of facilitating educational advancement for railway workers. He also showed particular interest in the welfare of retired employees presiding every year at a 'veterans' supper' at which he presented those present with a gift, a gesture which endeared him greatly to North Eastern staff. Their regard for him and his wife Mary was demonstrated at their silver wedding in June 1907 when they received several valuable presents from staff past and present.

Wilson's philanthropy extended beyond the railway service however. He donated a number of statues to one of the public parks of Gateshead and was active in encouraging boys' clubs in the town. One very fine cup presented to such a club as a trophy and subsequently stolen was discovered buried on a building site in the Gateshead area in the early 1960s. Returned to Wilson's grandson, Brigadier Geoffrey Worsdell, it was later presented to Wellington College where as the 'Wilson Worsdell Memorial Trophy' it is competed for each year at Bisley by the boys of the college.

Wilson was a member of the Local Board of Guardians in Gateshead and was made a Justice of the Peace for that town in 1907. He has been described as a 'fine, handsome man with a pleasant genial outlook on life' and was renowned for his good fellowship, positive attitude and approachability. He was particularly fond of making excursions at weekends with close colleagues to picturesque locations in Northumberland and was an enthusiastic fisherman, owning a house in Norway, at Framnes in the Voss district, which he used as the base for an annual fishing holiday. A very keen bowler throughout his adult life he was President of the Gateshead Bowling Green Club for some fifteen years up to his retirement. Like his brother William he was also an early motorist owning a vehicle, a 20/30 HP Fiat, as early as 1906. Evidently very generous even with this prized possession, he lent the car in that year to his son, 2nd Lt. Geoffrey Worsdell, newly commissioned in the Green Howards, who caused something of a stir by arriving at the Officers' Mess in it. He also allowed his niece Ella (Nee Cumine) and her husband Bob

Young to use it on honeymoon after their marriage at the Friends' Meeting House, Briggflatts.

Wilson was a man of very broad technical interests. In addition to his membership of the Institution of Mechanical Engineers, he was a Member of the Institute of Civil Engineers, of the Iron and Steel Institute and of the Institute of Naval Architects. In the year of his retirement he was elected President of the Association of Railway Locomotive Engineers and Carriage and Wagon Superintendents of Great Britain and Ireland. He took an active part in the International Railway Congress Association being a delegate to conferences in London in 1895, Paris in 1900 and Berne in 1910.

He retired from the post of Chief Mechanical Engineer of the NER on 31st May 1910, although he was appointed as a consultant at a salary of £2,000 per annum until the end of that year. It was said that this tribute surprised him somewhat but that he felt very gratified by it. At least two presentations were made to him on his retirement. Both were reported in the columns of the *Newcastle Evening Chronicle*. On Friday 27th May he was the guest of the salaried staff of his department at the Old Assembly Rooms, Newcastle. Vincent Raven, his successor, presided and in addition to outlining the progress made by the NER during Wilson's association with the company also warmly praised the philanthropic work of Wilson and Mary Worsdell in the community. The gift of an antique secretaire was a token of the staff's great regard for him.

A much larger gathering on Saturday 4th June saw a presentation to Wilson by the workmen of his department. This took place at a smoking concert held in the North Eastern Literary Institute. The Chairman, Mr J. Oliver, observed that Wilson was leaving Gateshead with the 'Y' class in the course of production and that he was sorry "that he was not staying to complete the alphabet". He added that since Wilson had come to Gateshead "there had been complete harmony in the...works". Mr Ben Slater made the presentation of a handsome cabinet gramophone and referred to Wilson's many qualities, and the esteem in which the railwaymen held him.

In reply Wilson said that far greater than the value of the gift he took great pleasure in the large number of subscribers (in excess of 1,300). He had intended to retire two years earlier but he was not permitted to do so by the directors. Now, at sixty, he felt he must grasp the opportunity of "a few years of enjoyment". Referring to the imminent transfer of much of the locomotive work to Darlington, he assured the meeting that he was not to blame for this, indeed neither was anyone else. The company required expanded workshop facilities and this was not feasible at the restricted Gateshead site at any reasonable cost, whereas land adjacent to the Darlington workshops was cheaply available for expansion there. The Gateshead works would continue to have an important role and would not be diminished in size. (In fairness to the workmen's argument, it is worth re-emphasising the point made in the last chapter concerning the lower wage rates prevailing at Darlington. Protests by the General Railway Workers Union at this time centred as much on this issue of wage reduction for staff being transferred as on the principle of the move itself).

Wilson congratulated the men for the "finest workmanship in the country", their engines held their own against any. He believed "that he retired with the goodwill of all", and if he had harshly treated anyone in his time he apologised. He especially singled out for thanks Ben Slater, for his work on the 'S' class engine which won the Gold Medal at the Paris Exhibition, and driver Bob Nicholson who had made the "record run of 124½ miles in 112 minutes" from Newcastle to Edinburgh in 1895. In conclusion Wilson said to applause, "I leave you with the knowledge that I have done my duty to the company. I wish my successor as much success in the future as you have obtained for me in the past".

On retirement Wilson and Mary moved to the South of England living at 'The Glebe', South Ascot, Berkshire. Wilson maintained an interest in railway matters becoming a director of a number of companies including the Westinghouse Brake and Signal Company. He and Mary also travelled. In late 1910 they visited Egypt where the now Lt. Geoffrey Worsdell was on his first overseas posting and in 1915 at the height of the First World War again visited their son, by now a captain, at Rawalpindi in the North West Frontier area of India. They spent four or five months there and were later to have responsibility briefly for their young grandson, also Geoffrey, just beginning at school back in England. This grandson, now Brigadier Geoffrey Worsdell (retired), born in 1913, recalls those times in India when a very small child. On outings he would be accompanied by a retinue of five: an English nanny and four Indian servants, an ayah, a guard and two bearers who carried him in a palanquin. Later on he remembers being taken from his grandfather's house at South Ascot to school in a gig soon after the end of the First World War and occasionally enjoying the special treat of a ride in grandfather's motor car.

Wilson Worsdell died suddenly at South Ascot on 14th April 1920 at the age of 69, leaving in the words of one commentator, 'a record of faithful and able service which gives him a lasting place among the famous men who have served the North Eastern Railway'. He was buried in All Souls

Wilson Worsdell - Egypt - 1910

churchyard, South Ascot and was joined there after her death, in nearby Bracknell in 1945, by his wife Mary. Wilson's memory was honoured by British Railways many years after his death. On Monday 30th October 1950 at a ceremony at Newcastle Central station, two of the LNER 'A1' class 'Pacific' locomotives were the subject of naming ceremonies. One commemorated Edward Fletcher, a great figure from the early days of the NER. The other was named 'Wilson Worsdell' by the Mayor of Gateshead (Alderman S. G. B. Tyrrell) in the presence of Ronald Worsdell, Wilson's nephew, himself a railwayman until his retirement four years previously.

Wilson Worsdell in retirement.

circa 1918

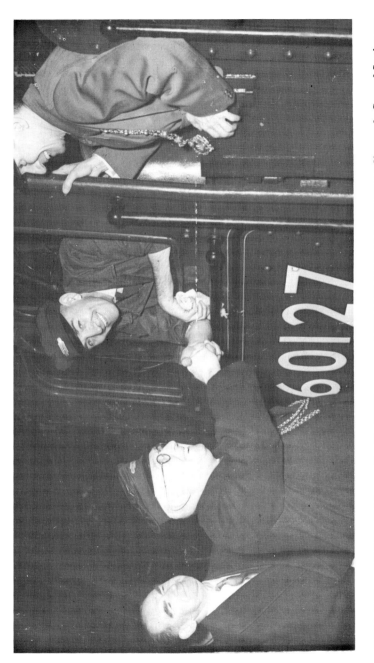

British Railways' 'A1' 'Pacific' locomotive No. 60127 was named *Wilson Worsdell* at a ceremony at Newcastle Central Station on Monday 30th October 1950.

VII

EPILOGUE—THE DESCENDANTS OF
THE ENGINEERS

A wide diversity of occupation

T hree of William Worsdell's five sons, born between 1867 and 1881, followed careers associated with railways but otherwise and thereafter a much wider diversity of occupation is observed in the Worsdell descendants. Two factors contributed to this, the first being the emancipation of Quakers as the 19th century progressed culminating in the repeal of the Corporation Act in 1871. This removed the last of the social and occupational restrictions against members of the sect. Secondly, the Worsdells themselves in the generation after the brothers William and Wilson seem, with the notable exception of one branch of the family, to have turned away from the Friends, increasingly embracing 'mainstream' christianity. For example, only one of William's sons, Wilson Crosfield Worsdell, appears to have been married at a Quaker Meeting House. Certainly the Worsdells born from the 1880s onwards appear to have felt none of the inhibitions and restrictions which affected their predecessors. This will become clear as we briefly consider the careers of just a few of the other members of the family.

The decendants of George Worsdell have to this day been the most loyal adherents to Quakerism in the family. George's only son Edward (1852-1908) was to become a distinguished Quaker scholar. Born in Warrington he was educated at Ackworth, took a BA Degree at London University in 1872 and studied further at Heidelberg between 1872 and 1875. Though raised and educated as a Friend he considered his 'conversion' to have taken place at the age of eighteen after which time he dedicated his life to the teaching ministry. He helped to found the Ackworth Adult School in 1874, and later taught in Stoke Newington and at the Friends' School at Bootham, York. He was from 1883 to 1888 tutor to the illustrious Quaker family of Fox at Falmouth in Cornwall and in 1889 married Rachel Tregelles Fox in that town, though he was by this time teaching in Scarborough. The couple lived at Scarborough and later Banbury.

Edward did not enjoy good health. As a young man in Heidelberg his health failed and he was victim, like his father before him, to severe insomnia. In the 1890s his eyesight began to fail and it was said of him that "at the prospect of blindness his one thought was that it would curtail his service". He was indeed forced to leave the teaching profession and take up a post at the Quaker owned Rowntree's cocoa works in York.

Edward was a prolific author on religious topics and published his *Gospel of Divine Help* in 1886. Noted locally in Yorkshire as an authority on Thackeray and Ruskin and for his appreciation of art, he was actively involved in theological summer schools. It was while addressing an 'adult school' in Darlington in March 1908 that he seized with a fatal illness and he died at the age of 56 leaving a widow and three young children. In a newspaper obituary it was said that with his death "the Society of Friends loses one of its ablest and foremost members". Edward's decendants have maintained their Quaker affiliation to the present day, two of his three grand-daughters marrying at Friends' Meeting Houses since the Second World War.

William Worsdell's eldest son Wilson Crosfield Worsdell (1867-1957) earned distinction in an altogether different field. Born in Pennsylvania, he returned to Crewe with his father in 1871 and as a boy developed an interest in natural history. After a Quaker boarding education at Egremont and, from 1882, at one of his father's old schools, Queenwood College in Hampshire, he worked in nurseries at Sheffield and in Holland. He studied botany at the Royal College of Science, South Kensington between 1891-93. Appointed demonstrator in botany at University College, London, he was involved in the work of the Natural History Museum and of the Jodrell Laboratory at the Royal Botanic Gardens, Kew. He was elected a Fellow of the Linnean Society in 1898. In February 1909 he went to South Africa for a year as acting Professor of Botany at the South African College, Cape Town and returned to that country in 1912-13 as acting lecturer in botany at Victoria College, Stellenbosch. Whilst in South Africa he travelled extensively collecting plants including a visit to South West Africa. His collection of South African plants is kept at Birmingham University.

The later part of his career was spent in research at the Jodrell Laboratory, Kew notably into the stem structure of dicotyledons. His magnum opus, *Principles of Plant Teratology* was published in two volumes in 1915-16. After seven years of retirement he returned to Kew assisting Dr Stapf in the

Wilson Crosfield Worsdell (1867-1957). An eminent botanist, he was the eldest son of T. W. Worsdell and was born at Altoona, Pennsylvania.

preparation of the 'Index Londinensis' and following Stapf's death he edited two supplementary volumes of the Index in 1941, for which the Royal Horticultural Society awarded him the Veitch Memorial Medal. Wilson Crosfield Worsdell married Dorothy Johnson in 1920 at the comparatively advanced age of 52. The ceremony took place at the Friends' Meeting House, Ashford. He died at Twickenham on 29th October 1957 having recently passed his 90th birthday.

Of the three sons of William Worsdell who worked in the field of railways, the eldest Henry (1869-1945) had the most varied and colourful career. He was born in Pennsylvania and was apprenticed to the North Eastern Railway (of which his father was, of course, Locomotive Superintendent) on leaving school. He served the company at a number of places amongst which was Carlisle. From about 1900 to 1903 he was undermanager of the company's Carriage and Wagon Works at York and later joined the Great Central Railway at their Gorton, Manchester workshops, living at Marple in Cheshire. Gorton Works was being expanded and re-equipped at this time and Henry was largely responsible for the work, reporting to the

Locomotive Superintendent J. G. Robinson. By the time of his spell at Gorton, Henry, in his thirties and not many years married, had clearly drifted away from Quakerism. In a perhaps not intentionally funny letter to his father from Marple he reveals that "I have taken to going to Meeting again" but then goes on to explain the uncomfortable time he had there on one occasion owing to the mischievous antics of his dog, who escaped from his place of confinement and could not be kept still.

In about 1907 Henry joined the Brush Electrical Engineering Co. Ltd of Loughborough, a private company specialising in railway and tramway equipment and still a major force in the industry to this day. He was unhappy there, however, and soon joined the South Indian Railway as manager of their works at Negapatam, a coastal town in Madras Province. He retired from this company in the early 1920s as Deputy Head of the Mechanical and Engineering Department and returned to England settling at 'Almery Garth', a substantial house in the Bootham district of York. He died in Highgate, London in 1946.

Between 1920 and 1922 Henry described as 'of Negapatam, Madras Presidency' applied for and was granted a patent for an improvement in the design of "axle boxes for railways and the like".

Two of Henry's younger brothers Robert (1873-1966) and Ronald (1881-1974) had rather uneventful careers in comparison, both spending the whole of their working lives on the North Eastern Railway and its successor the LNER. Robert was a pupil at Gateshead Works and served for 34 years in all, at Darlington, in charge of the surburban electric railway at Newcastle and as manager of Shildon Wagon Works. Ronald gave more than 40 years service in the operating department at such places as Tyne Dock, Washington and Ripon.

Henry Worsdell's three sons have all achieved distinction but in areas far removed from railway engineering. The eldest Cedric (born 1902) started as a drawing office pupil with the North Eastern Railway and was briefly a volunteer engine driver for the LNER during the General Strike of 1926. He later worked for the Conservative Party for many years. After war service with the Royal Air Force he was for two years constituency secretary and agent to Sir Winston Churchill, then MP for Woodford, Essex. Guy Worsdell (1908-1978) was a professional artist and engraver of note who between 1960 and 1970 exhibited five works—wood engravings, paintings and pencil drawings—at the Royal Academy. He lived in Kensington in the later years of his life. The youngest son, Anthony (born 1920) is a professional musician. Trained at the Guildhall School of Music he has played with a number of orchestras and ensembles as a clarinetist. Now

Epilogue

LETTERS TO BE ADDRESSED TO:—

THE CHIEF MECHANICAL ENGINEER,

LONDON & NORTH EASTERN RAILWAY,

H. N. GRESLEY,
Chief Mechanical Engineer.

TELEGRAMS:
"GRESLEY, NORTHEASTERN,
RAIL, LONDON"

TELEPHONE:
NORTH 4200.

KING'S CROSS STATION,

LONDON, N.1.

11th June, 1926.

Dear Sir,

I thought you would like to have a souvenir to remind you of the part you played in the General Strike, 1926, when you acted as a Volunteer Locomotive Engine Driver on the London and North Eastern Railway.   I therefore have pleasure in sending you the enclosed photograph of one of our latest Express Engines of the "Pacific" type.

The ready and willing way in which you and other Volunteers rallied to the help of the Railway Companies in their endeavour to get trains running for essential services was beyon all praise, and was undoubtedly one of the principal causes leading to the early termination of the General Strike.

Yours faithfully,

N.H.Gresley

C. Worsdell Esq.,
    21, Castlegate,—— *driving Scots express "Flying Fox"*
        YORK.

The letter of thanks written after the General Strike of 1926 by H. N. (later Sir Nigel) Gresley to the volunteer engine driver, Cedric Worsdell.

living in Shropshire, he plays as a free lance and recitalist as well as teaching clarinet and saxophone over a wide area. His musical versatility also extends to the repairing and tuning of organs and pianos.

Cedric Worsdell's only daughter, Caroline Bingham (born 1938) adds literary distinction to the list of Worsdell accomplishments. After a Quaker, convent and public schooling she read history at Bristol University. She won acclaim with the publication of her first book *The Making of a King: the early years of James VI and I* in 1968 and has since published several more volumes of historical biography mainly, but not exclusively, concerned with Scottish subjects, as well as an anthology of Scottish historical verse. Her works include *The Life and Times of Edward II*, *The Stewart Kingdom of Scotland 1371-1603*, *The Crowned Lions* — about the early Plantaganet Kings, and a two volume biography of 'James VI and I' published in 1979 and 1981. She has also written *The History of Royal Holloway College, 1886-1986* (1987).

We have seen that Wilson Worsdell married in church rather than in a Friends' Meeting House although he did not break with the Friends, transferring his membership to the Newcastle Monthly Meeting when he moved to Gateshead in 1883. His son Geoffrey (1883-1946) received what might be called a conventional Anglican education at Charterhouse and Trinity College, Cambridge. Geoffrey was to pursue a military career, something that would have been unthinkable had he been brought up in the Quaker tradition. Commissioned in the Green Howards (19th Foot) in 1906, he attained the rank of Captain (Brevet Major) and saw active service in Mesopotamia, Kurdistan and Afghanistan. He was in India in 1915, being visited there by his father, but had returned to home service by 1923 or 1924. During the Second World War he served in the Chief Censor's Department in London. He was appointed an officer of the Order of the British Empire (OBE).

Captain Worsdell's sons also followed military careers both being educated at Wellington College, a favourite school for Army sons. The youngest Kenneth went not into the Army, but via Cranwell into the Royal Air Force. He was killed during the Battle of Britain in 1940 whilst serving on night fighters with 219 Squadron. The elder son, Geoffrey (born 1913) chose the Army. After Sandhurst he was commissioned in his father's regiment, the Green Howards, in 1933. He transferred to the Royal Army Ordnance Corps in 1942. He saw active service in India before the Second World War, in Europe during that conflict and in Korea and Malaya afterwards. Promoted to Brigadier in 1962 he was Aide-de-Camp to Her Majesty Queen Elizabeth II from 1966 to 1968 in which year he retired.

In selecting the Worsdell descendants above the present author has sought not to discriminate between members or branches of the family but merely to illustrate the way in which the descendents of Thomas Clarke Worsdell II, who for three generations on the male side were almost obsessively concerned with railway and engineering matters, have, in the succeeding three generations, embraced a much wider choice of vocation often with considerable success. Perhaps it is not too fanciful to detect the Quaker virtues and sense of duty still informing the actions of the twentieth century members of the family.

A portion of the 'Quaker Tapestry' devoted to early railways. The Worsdell name is honoured in the central bottom arch. *(Quaker Tapestry Scheme)*

An appropriate postcript to this biography is provided by the recent completion of the 'Quaker Tapestry'. A ten year project inspired by the Bayeux Tapestry, it celebrates Quakerism through the medium of 75 embroidered panels. More than 2,000 people in eight countries were involved in its creation, culminating in public displays at the Royal Festival Hall, London, in the spring of 1990 and at Bayeux in the summer.

The role of the Worsdells in early railway development is acknowledged in the science and industry panels and it is pleasing to record the connection of family members with the Leicester Friends' contribution to the tapestry. Dorothy Dodsworth, a member of Leicester meeting, and her sister Ruth Pashley, also a Friend, made available Worsdell source material to the Leicester Group. Mrs Dodsworth and Mrs Pashley are great-granddaughters of George Worsdell, the Warrington ironmaster, and granddaughters of Edward Worsdell, the Quaker scholar.

APPENDIX I

Locomotives designed by T. W. Worsdell

(i) GREAT EASTERN RAILWAY

GER classification	Wheel arrangement	Year introduced	Number built	LNER/BR classification
G14	2-4-0	1882	20	—
Y14	0-6-0	1883	289	J15
G15	0-4-0	1883	10	Y6
M15	2-4-2T	1884	160	F4
G16	4-4-0	1884	11	—

(ii) NORTH EASTERN RAILWAY

NER classification	Wheel arrangement	Simple/ compound	Year introduced	Number built	LNER/BR classification
A	2-4-2T	S	1886	60	F8
B	0-6-2T	C	1886	51	—
B1	0-6-2T	S	1886	11	N8
C	0-6-0	C	1886	171	—
C1	0-6-0	S	1886	30	J21
D	2-4-0	C	1886	2	—
E	0-6-0T	S	1886	120	J71
F1	4-4-0	S	1887	10	D22
F	4-4-0	C	1887	25	D22
G	2-4-0	S	1887	20	D23
H	0-4-0T	S	1888	22	Y7
H1	0-6-0T	S	1888	2	J78
I	4-2-2	C	1888	10	—
J	4-2-2	C	1889	10	—
K	0-4-0T	S	1890	5	Y8

APPENDIX II

Locomotives designed by Wilson Worsdell

NER classification	Wheel arrangement	Year introduced	Number built	LNER/BR classification
L	0-6-0T	1891	10	J73
M1	4-4-0	1892	20	D17/1
M	4-4-0	1893	1	—
N	0-6-2T	1893	20	N9
O	0-4-4T	1894	110	G5
P	0-6-0	1894	70	J24
P1	0-6-0	1898	140	J25
P2	0-6-0	1904	50	J26
P3	0-6-0	1906	115	J27
Q	4-4-0	1896	30	D17/2
Q1	4-4-0	1896	2	D18
H2	0-6-0T	1897	3	J79
E1	0-6-0T	1898	113	J72
R	4-4-0	1899	60	D20
290	0-6-0T	1899	60	J77
S	4-6-0	1899	40	B13
S1	4-6-0	1901	5	B14
T	0-8-0	1901	40	Q5
T1	0-8-0	1902	50	Q5
U	0-6-2T	1902	20	N10
V	4-4-2	1903	10	C6
4CC	4-4-2	1906	2	C8
W	4-6-0T	1907	10	A6
R1	4-4-0	1908	10	D21
X	4-8-0T	1909	15	T1
V1	4-4-2	1910	10	C6

APPENDIX III

Extant Worsdell Locomotives

Classification	Locomotive number	Designer	Location
GER 'Y14'	GER 564/BR 65462	T.W.W	North Norfolk Railway, Sheringham
NER 'C'	NER 876/BR 65033	T.W.W	North of England Open Air Museum, Beamish Hall, County Durham
NER 'H'	NER 1310	T.W.W	Middleton Railway, Leeds
NER 'H'	LNER 985/BR 68088	T.W.W	Great Central Railway, Loughborough
NER 'MI'	NER 1621	W.W	National Railway Museum, York
NER 'P3'	NER 2392/BR 65894	W.W	North Yorkshire Moors Railway, Grosmont
NER 'EI'	BR 69023	W.W	North Yorkshire Moors Railway, Grosmont
NER '66'	NER 66, 'AEROLITE'	*	National Railway Museum, York

* originally built by Edward Fletcher (1869), rebuilt by T. W. Worsdell (1886) and Wilson Worsdell (1902).

APPENDIX IV

Some known products of Thomas Worsdell's Birmingham Works (1858-64)

1858	4 Treble purchase crabs to lift 25 tons for Bombay, Baroda and Central India Railway (BBCIR)
1858	10 crabs to lift 20 tons for BBCIR
1858	6 crabs to lift 15 tons for BBCIR
1859	4 crabs to lift 8 tons for BBCIR
1858	Pulley Blocks
Dec. 1858	5 six ton coal wagons
1859	1 Horse mill pump for Wood & Sons, Bath Street, Birmingham
1859	6 cast iron jacks for Tanatt & Co., 46 Ann Street, Birmingham
1859	50 broad gauge wagons for the Vale of Neath Railway Company
1861	2 10″ screw cutting lathes with 14′ 0″ beds
Oct. 1861	4 fixed steam cranes to lift 30 cwt.
Oct. 1861	2 fixed steam cranes to lift 45 cwt.
1861	1 travelling steam crane to lift 3 tons
Mar. 1862	1 four coupled saddle tank locomotive named 'Dwarf' for Savin and Ward, contractors, of Oswestry
Oct. 1863	1 four coupled saddle tank locomotive named 'Tanat' for R. S. France, contractor, of Shrewsbury
1864	1 fixed steam crane to lift 8 tons
1864	1 travelling steam crane to lift 6 tons
1864	1 travelling steam crane to lift 45 cwt.
1864	1 steam road roller for J.P. of Calcutta
1864	1 18″ sliding and screw cutting lathe
1864	2 100 ton hydraulic girder testers

APPENDIX V

Patents granted to the Worsdells

Patentee	Patent Number and date	Description
Nathaniel Worsdell	7,528 (1838)	Apparatus to facilitate the conveyance of mail bags and other parcels on railways or roads.
Thomas Worsdell	10,892 (1845)	Apparatus to be attached to and employed in connection with railway carriages.
" "	12,853 (1849)	Manufacture of envelopes and cases; tools and machinery used therein.
" "	1,249 (1855)	Lifting jacks.
" "	1,531 (1864)	An improved pulley or sheave block.
T. W. Worsdell and James Smith	1,646 (1871)	Spark arrestors.
T. W. Worsdell	999 (1885)	Compound steam engines.
T. W. Worsdell and others	1,000 (1885)	Draught and dust excluders for windows.
T. W. Worsdell	4,661 (1887)	Compound engines.
T. W. Worsdell, A. Von Borries and R. H. Lapage	7,647 (1892)	Compound engines.
" " "	6,487 (1900)	Engine valves.
" " "	22,906 (1900)	Locomotives etc.
Wilson Worsdell and Walter Reuben Preston	16,980 (1907)	Locomotive blast pipes
Henry Worsdell	159,183 (1921)	Railway vehicle axle boxes

APPENDIX VI

Menu at Nathaniel Worsdell's Presentation Dinner, North Western Hotel, Liverpool, 10 February 1881

Les Huitres Naturel
------* * *------

Potages

Tortue Claire
Creme de Volaille à la Royale
------* * *------

Hors d'oeuvres

Salade d'Anchois
------* * *------

Poissons

Saumon Sauce Parsil
Filets de Sole à la Normande
Blanchailles
------* * *------

Entrees

Crepinettes à la Russe
Ris de Veau à la Pompadour
Filets de Poulets aux Truffe
------* * *------

Releves

Quartier d'Agneau
Filets de Boef Piqué à la Jardiniere
Dinde Braise et Langue de Boeuf
------* * *------

Rots

Canards Sauvage
Bacasses
Mayonnaise de Homard en Aspic
------* * *------

Entremets

Pouding à la Royale
Petits choux à la Creme
Pouding Glacé
Macedoine de fruits
Gelée au Madere
Eau de Citron et Fraise
Dessert

APPENDIX VII

Agreements to Develop and Promote the Worsdell-von Borries Compounding System

The texts of the two agreements have survived by which William Worsdell and August von Borries sought jointly to exploit their respective patents for improvements in compound engines.

A partnership agreement drawn up in Hanover and dated 4th May 1886 laid down that royalties, after expenses, were to be shared equally between the two partners. Any expenditure in excess of receipts in the early years was to be disbursed by William Worsdell. Richard Herbert Lapage and Messrs Taite and Carlton were to be agents for the combined patents and were to receive a commission of 10% of the net profits.

A subsequent agreement dated 6th July 1886 and of British origin nullified the first agreement and another, dating from May 1885 between von Borries, Lapage and Friedrich Carl Glaser. The new arrangement, specifically not a partnership, was between William Worsdell, von Borries of '15 Herrni Strasse, Hanover, in the Kingdom of Prussia', Lapage, and John Charles Taite and Thomas William Carlton, trading as Taite and Carlton of 63 Queen Victoria Street, London.

Under the agreement a royalty of £50 was to be paid collectively to the signatories for each locomotive of the Worsdell-von Borries type constructed, having a high pressure cylinder in excess of 13in. diameter and £25 for those of less measurement. A royalty of £10 to £20 was to be charged for each tramway engine built on the principle. Locomotives manufactured in Germany, Austria, Russia, Italy and Belgium were excluded from the terms of the agreement at this time. The firm of Dubs and Co of Glasgow were said to be engaged in constructing three compound engines on the principle at the time of draughting and were not to be charged royalties on these, and a number of tramway engines 'under negotiation' with Beyer, Peacock & Co of Manchester were to be similarly royalty free.

The royalties were to be divided: Worsdell 33%, von Borries 33%, Lapage 27%, Taite & Carlton 7%. Messrs Taite and Carlton were to keep accounts for the venture and there was to be a special bank account, 'The Compound Engine Account'. Lapage and Taite and Carlton were to bear the main responsibility of promoting the inventions and the costs of this were to be born by them.

The agreement was clearly expected to be of long standing, subject to the limitations of patent law. Future improvements to the principle by any of the parties were covered by its provisions, as was a procedure for arbitration in the case of disputes and rules of inheritance in the event of the death of a signatory.

ACKNOWLEDGEMENTS

The author is very grateful to a large number of people who have assisted him in producing this biography. I owe a great debt to members of the Worsdell family for their kind hospitality and for making family records available to me: Mr & Mrs Cedric Worsdell (York), Brigadier Geoffrey Worsdell (Bognor Regis), Mr and Mrs H. M. Lattimer (Maidenhead), Mr Robin Worsdell and family (Huddersfield), Miss Mary Worsdell (Twyford) and Peter and Carol Lattimer (East Finchley). In particular the family tree produced by Brigadier Worsdell, the fruit of years of genealogical research, has repeatedly been the source of valuable information and has made my task very much easier.

I am most indebted to the following for very generous assistance with illustrations for the book:

The Worsdell family

The North Woolwich Old Station Museum (Mr T. Turbin)

The Great Eastern Railway Society

Mr C. P. Atkins and the library staff at the National Railway Museum, York

Mr Geoffrey Horsman of Leeds

and most particularly to Mr Kenneth L. Taylor of Darlington for furnishing me with prints from his huge collection of North Eastern Railway subjects.

The staffs of the following Institutions have also helped me with all manner of queries in a most efficient manner:

Warrington Reference Library

Lancashire County Record Office, Preston

Birmingham Central Library (Local Studies Department)

Newcastle upon Tyne Central Library(Local Studies Department)

Public Record Office, Kew, London

British Library, Newspaper Library, Colindale, London

British Library, Science Reference Library, Holborn, London

Friends House Library, London

Science Museum Library, South Kensington, London

I am greatly indebted to Paul, Jane and James Hunt for word-processing my near-illegible manuscript with such speed and efficiency, to Peter Lattimer for suggesting the project to me in the first place, and to his father, H. M. Lattimer, for much practical help and encouragement. My friend Tom Worsley spared me a good deal of effort by making his extensive collection of books on railway matters available to me.

I thank all these people; any mistakes in the final text are entirely my own.

BIBLIOGRAPHY

Apart from family and other papers and the various archives, the author has drawn heavily on the following published works in the preparation of this biographical study:

Cecil J. Allen, *The Great Eastern Railway* (5th edition, 1968)

Cecil J. Allen, *The North Eastern Railway*, (1964)

W .H. Chaloner, *The Social and Economic Development of Crewe, 1780-1923*, (1950)

K. Hoole, *North Road Locomotive Works Darlington, 1863-1966*, (1967)

J. S. MacLean, *The Locomotives of the North Eastern Railway 1854-1905*, (1905)

O. S. Nock, *The Locomotives of the North Eastern Railway*, (1974 edition)

R. H. G. Thomas, *The Liverpool and Manchester Railway*, (1980)

W. A. Tuplin, *North Eastern Steam*, (1970)

David Burns Windsor, *The Quaker Enterprise*, (1980)

The following works also furnished much useful information:

Anon, More reminiscences of Stratford (in *The Locomotive Magazine, Railway Carriage and Wagon Review*, 15 May, 1936)

Anon, *Famous Locomotive Engineers-10, 'T.W.Worsdell'* (in *The Locomotive Magazine, Railway Carriage and Wagon Review*, 15 April, 1939)

W. H. Chaloner, *The Worsdells and the Early Railway System* (in *Railway Magazine*, October 1938)

Hunter Davies, *George Stephenson* (1975)

C. Hamilton Ellis, *Last Years of the Tennants* (in *Railway Magazine*, August 1984)

Martin Evans, *Atlantic Era* (1961)

Dr. R. J. Irving, *Unsung hero of the North Eastern Railway* (Alexander McDonnell) (in *Railway Magazine*, December 1984)

James W. Lowe, *British Steam Locomotive Builders* (1975)

Norman MacDonald, *NER officials visit to the United States* (in *The Locomotive Magazine, Railway Carriage and Wagon Review*, 10 Jan, 1903)

John Punshon, *Portrait in Grey* (1984)

'RCR', *Famous North Eastern Men — Wilson Worsdell* (in *North Eastern and Scottish Railway Magazine*, Volume XV, 1925)

Brian Reed, *Crewe Locomotive Works and its Men* (1982)

Stuart J. Reid, *Sir Richard Tangye* (1908)

L. T. C. Rolt, *George and Robert Stephenson* (1960)

W. O. Skeat, *George Stephenson, the Engineer and his letters* (1973)

Gillian Tindall, *The Fields Beneath* (1980)

W. W. Tomlinson, *The North Eastern Railway, its Rise and Development* (1914)

E. J. Tyler, *Massey Bromley on the Great Eastern Railway* (in *Railway World*, July 1984)

John Vaizey, *The History of British Steel* (1974)

Rodney Weaver, *Francis William Webb, a Reappraisal* (in *Railway World*, September and October 1986)

Index